Guide for Snow and Ice Control

American Association of State Highway and Transportation Officials

444 North Capitol Street, NW, Suite 249
Washington, DC 20001
(202) 624-5800 (tel)
(202) 624-5806 (fax)
www.aashto.org (web)

ISBN: 1-56051-101-X

Winter Maintenance Policy Coordinating Committee

Chairman: PATRICK C. HUGHES, Minnesota

AASHTO Representatives
GARY HOFFMAN, Pennsylvania
ANDY BAILEY, Virginia
LELAND D. SMITHSON, Iowa
CLAYTON SULLIVAN, Idaho

AASHTO Lead State Program
(RWIS/Anti-Icing Program)
RICK NELSON

AASHTO State Liaison
KEN KOBETSKY

SICOP Coordinator
RODNEY PLETAN
State Maintenance Engineer
Minnesota Department of Transportation
395 John Ireland Blvd
M.S. 630, RM 803
St. Paul, Minnesora 55155
(612) 297-3593

FHWA Representative
DON STEINKE

NACE Representative
DAVE GRAVENKAMP

APWA Representative
LARRY FREVERT

Transportation Research Board
WILFRID NIXON

Table of Contents

Summary

State highway maintenance officials recognize that the adoption of a systematic approach to snow and ice control using available technology and research while implementing a proactive decision making process improves service and reduces costs. Snow and ice control is one of the most important functions performed by maintenance forces in many state, county, and local government highway agencies. This winter maintenance function is frequently resource intensive and often strains maintenance budgets. For some agencies, snow and ice control is the single largest line item in the highway maintenance budget

Recognizing the potential savings and the opportunity to improve winter maintenance in general, the AASHTO Board of Directors, acting on recommendations by the AASHTO Standing Committee on Highways and the AASHTO Highway Subcommittee on Maintenance, approved an administrative resolution in November 1994 establishing a winter maintenance program. One element of this program supports the establishment of a project under the National Cooperative Highway Research Program (NCHRP) to develop a comprehensive guide for snow and ice control. As a result, a comprehensive outline of a proposed guide was developed under NCHRP Project 20-7, Task 71, "Winter Maintenance Program."

In 1998, this *Guide for Snow and Ice Control* was developed under NCHRP Project 20-7, Task 83 based on the outline developed in the earlier project. The authors of this guide used basic snow and ice control concepts and principles as a starting point and suggested new technologies and different and innovative procedures and practices that can help reduce costs and improve service. The guide provides a training tool to help operators, supervisors, and managers select and implement new methods or technologies to effectively and efficiently deal with snow and ice conditions and provide road users with safe conditions and timely information to make trip decisions.

Figure 1. Snow blower operating in New York State.

The guide is not intended to specify any single standard, procedure, material, equipment, or regulation for all programs; rather it provides guidance for organizations responsible for roadway snow and ice control programs by presenting principles and practices for various environmental and operational conditions. The guide discusses state-of-the-art technologies and processes pertaining to snow and ice control for consideration and adoption by AASHTO member departments and other organizations responsible for roadway snow and ice control programs. Some of the material presented in the guide reflects the experience of the authors or are recognized practices that are not necessarily documented in writing. Individual agencies are expected to implement practices and procedures that allow them to provide the level of service established in agency policies and guidelines.

Characteristics of this Guide

This guide has been developed for use by organizations responsible for roadway snow and ice control programs, presenting principles and practices for various climatological, environmental, and operational conditions. The guide also provides concepts, processes, and references that may serve as a checklist and resource for agencies developing and refining a comprehensive snow and ice control program. The terms *roadways, highways, roads,* and *streets* are used throughout the guide with the intent that policies and procedures discussed in the guide are usually applicable to all levels of jurisdiction.

The guide contains ten chapters organized in a systematic fashion to provide insight into the components of a snow and ice control operations and management. Chapter 1 discusses the purpose and principles of a winter snow and ice control maintenance program, including agency responsibilities to their customers and accountability. It provides an overview of environmental considerations, describes the impact of weather on roads, and concludes with a discussion on the importance of new technology and innovation in improving snow and ice control.

Chapter 2 describes the need for good communications. Communications within an agency are crucial, but are also important with the public, media, and other agencies. Chapter 2 also describes the development of policies and procedures to establish a level of service (LOS) and the means to attain that level, the importance of monitoring agency performance, and methods for assessing performance.

Chapters 3 through 5 discuss the topics of labor, equipment, and material (LEM) respectively, as related to snow and ice control. Chapter 3 details the importance of good, comprehensive training programs; discusses general personnel management issues, options, and concerns for establishing duty schedules; describes compensation issues for winter work forces; and includes a brief discussion of substance abuse. Chapter 4 covers equipment issues, including the types used for on-the-road operations, support systems, maintenance requirements, and equipment acquisition. Chapter 5 describes snow and ice control material (abrasives and chemicals) acquisition considerations, including storage, handling, and inventory of such materials as well as issues associated with the use of appropriate materials for various weather and pavement conditions.

Chapter 6 provides insight into the development and applications of weather information, specifically road weather information system (RWIS) information for snow and ice control. It points out that the knowledge of expected weather and pavement conditions can provide snow and ice control decision makers a tool to manage LEM more efficiently and effectively, and provide a better level of service or an established level of service at potentially reduced cost.

Chapter 7 describes the conduct of snow and ice control operations, including pre-storm preparation, during-the-storm operations, and post-storm activities. Chapter 8 continues the discussion of storm operations by presenting a concept of total storm management. Although used primarily for anti-icing, the total storm management concept can be used for all snow and ice control strategies.

Chapter 9 gives insight into safety and liability issues that need to be considered when developing agency snow and ice control plans and procedures. Safety is discussed in terms of both road users and maintenance crews. Material is presented from a fleet safety standpoint. Liability and risk management issues are discussed, including references to helpful materials for use in a safety program. Finally, Chapter 10 describes special topics, such as road design for maintainability and dealing with special hazards, and reiterates the need to consider environmental issues.

The guide includes three appendices that provide supplemental information, including:

❋ a comprehensive bibliography of publications of interest to snow and ice control professionals to help managers develop policies, guidelines, and procedural manuals;

❋ examples of processes and procedures that can be used by roadway maintenance agencies such as a suggested training curriculum, sample contract for snow and ice control services, sample public information release, spreader calibration procedures, vehicle maintenance checklist, and examples of materials available from Local Technical Assistance Programs (LTAP) Centers;

❊ sample material and equipment specifications that can be used by roadway maintenance agencies.

In addition, a list of references used in preparing the guide is located at the end of each chapter, although readers are encouraged to continually check for new information regarding snow and ice control management and practices.

The guide is a useful resource for winter maintenance program administrators, managers, and operators, and a tool for training winter maintenance personnel. This guide is a "work in progress" and will be revised as new technologies and innovations become available.

References

Winter Maintenance Program: Plans for Snow and Ice Control Guide and Snow and Ice Pooled Fund Cooperative Program, Project No. 20-7(71), National Cooperative Highway Research Program, Transportation Research Board, Washington, D.C., June 1996.

1 Purpose and Principles of a Winter Maintenance Program

Snow and ice control is a critical part of many highway maintenance agencies, but only one element in a complete winter maintenance program. In some agencies, snow and ice control is the largest single-line item in highway maintenance, determining budgetary allocations for the number of personnel, types of equipment, and materials to be used based upon anticipated needs for the coming year. Additional winter maintenance may also include pothole and damage repairs, drainage cleaning, debris removal, brush removal, facility inventory and condition assessments, certain types of bridge work, fabrication of units for summer work, and equipment maintenance. As a result, transportation agencies are typically responsible for:

* creating and maintaining common transportation facilities (roadways, bicycle and pedestrian paths and sidewalks, airfields and runways);

* resources committed and responsibilities undertaken in snow and ice control programs;

* safety and well being of people using and maintaining transportation systems;

* environment surrounding transportation facilities;

* ensuring mobility and connectivity, and

* national defense.

In addition, winter weather has a direct impact upon local and national economies. A Federal Highway Administration spokesman highlighted the urgency of snow and ice control when he stated that "highways are the warehouses of industry." Manufacturers, wholesalers, and retailers rely on surface transportation to deliver parts, commodities, and goods to the point of manufacture or sale when needed. Industry and commerce can grind to a halt if these "just-in-time" deliveries, a practice employed by 45 percent of industry, are delayed or cannot move.

Impact of Winter Weather

The economic impact of effective snow and ice control is not well documented, however, the impact of a lack of snow and ice control, as well as the activities themselves, is well understood. Studies in Sweden and the United States indicate that snow and ice control activities significantly reduce accident rates. Winter weather is also responsible for increases in travel time, fuel consumption, and insurance costs as well as decreases in mobility and throughput on the roadways, and productivity and commerce in general.

Climate and Weather

Climate is the weather of a locality averaged over a time period (usually thirty years) plus statistics which include extremes in weather behavior recorded during that same period or even an entire period or record. Climate can vary over small areas, such as in the Pacific Northwest where rapid transitions in elevation and proximity to water sources change precipitation patterns drastically. Climate can also be similar over large areas such as states or regions.

Planning and budgeting for snow and ice control require knowledge of the climate. A typical winter can usually be defined in order to establish resource requirements. Different winter indices, specially calculated climate variables, have been developed to help managers assess their needs and perhaps to explain overruns. However, the wealth of experience of the people within an agency also can be used to establish a similar baseline for a particular climate.

Weather, in contrast to climate, is the state of the atmosphere at a given time. Weather can be expressed terms of temperature, humidity, precipitation, and wind. It can be thought of as a collection of phenomena that affect nature, such as tornadoes, thunderstorms, precipitation, or obstructions to vision.

For snow and ice control, weather provides both atmospheric conditions and resultant pavement conditions. Snow and ice control personnel have to deal with snow accumulation on roadways, as well as the formation of black ice, frost, and snow pack. Weather indirectly causes the problems, whereas pavement temperature contributes directly to ice or snow bonding to pavement. Additional discussion of the affect of weather on road conditions is provided in chapter 6.

Objectives of Snow and Ice Control Programs

Policy Guidance for Program Planning

All agencies responsible for snow and ice control should have written policies and guidelines that document the intent, capabilities, and procedures of their snow and ice control program. Such policies provide a common understanding between customers and the agency of what can be expected when weather and pavement conditions warrant implementing the snow and ice control activities. Guidelines provide the mangers and operators with a basis for conducting specific operations under certain conditions, such as safety guidelines for using equipment and post-storm clean up. An effective snow and ice control program should include:

* a vision of the goals and expectations, including the level of service that should be documented in agency policies and guidelines used as a basis for all planning and snow and ice control operations;

* assignment of priorities for snow and ice control resource allocations and maintenance activities to achieve the established service levels;

* fiscal accountability to the users/stakeholders/providers of funds (elected and appointed officials and the public) to ensure that agencies use labor, equipment and materials efficiently and effectively in achieving the service level goals;

* understanding of legal responsibilities and constraints with respect to snow and ice control;

* protection of the environment through wise use of chemicals and abrasives to minimize the impact on soil, vegetation, water, animals, and the infrastructure;

* education of the public to ensure understanding of the capabilities and limitations of snow and ice control, thus creating a positive relationship and fostering public support;

* willingness to implement changes and innovations to improve operations by adopting technological advances in equipment, chemicals, and methods for improving the conduct of snow and ice control.

It is important to gather a variety of input when developing policy. Policy development and periodic review should be a cooperative and participative process with involved parties, including customers, media, highway agency management, equipment operators, contractors where applicable, and other agencies responsible for emergency management services, travel, and tourism. Policies must be practical and achievable. Serious liability concerns arise if the policy promises more than what can be delivered under all conditions. In addition, all employees need to know and understand adopted policies. A coordinated policy, agreed upon by the agency and its customers, will stand the test of time and bad weather incidents.

When developing the policy, it is difficult, but necessary, to consider the balance between cost, public and operational safety, and environmental issues. Budgetary constraints increasingly become a center of focus, while the customers seem to demand more service. Yet more service, especially dealing with snow and ice control and de-icing chemical applications, can potentially impact the environment. The policy must clearly define reasons for conducting (or not conducting) certain activities.

Environmental Considerations

Managers and operators need to maintain a special environmental awareness and sensitivity in the use of chemicals and other products and procedures for snow and ice control. Special consideration needs to be given to:

* controlling runoff from roadway applications;

* proper storage of chemicals and abrasives;

* protecting groundwater, including wells and aquifers;

* protecting vegetation;

* protecting maintenance facilities and equipment against weather, corrosion;

* protecting transportation facilities (bridges, pavement, appurtenances) against corrosion;

* protecting employees from the potential dangers associated with snow and ice control materials; and

* minimizing air quality and highway safety impacts associated with the use of abrasives;

* minimizing the effects of traffic congestion and studded tire dust on air quality;

❄ protecting surface water quality;

❄ protecting habitat quality; and

❄ coordinating with permitting agencies, e.g., Metropolitan Planning Organization, National Forest Service, and local departments of ecology and natural resources.

Level of Service

Because of the need for continued mobility and safety on the roads, it is important that snow and ice control programs establish a level of service that satisfies the customers and is attainable with available budget and resources.   Level of service (LOS) refers to operational guidelines establishing maintenance activities associated with the prevention and removal of snow and ice from roadways. LOS may establish a prescribed end-of-storm condition, intermediate stages acceptable while obtaining that condition, or the frequency of snow and ice control maintenance operations.   LOS results from an analysis of:

❄ agency snow and ice control policy;

❄ road classifications;

❄ traffic data;

❄ maintenance coverage time periods defined for various operations, including clean-up operations;

❄ equipment types and amounts;

❄ location of facilities;

❄ personnel rules and regulations;

❄ materials used; and

❄ special circumstances and conditions.

Examples of levels of service, compiled from difference agencies, are shown in table 1. Although a suggested description of road condition is given for each road classification, some agencies prefer to specify only the coverage time periods for snow and ice operations.

Table 1. Examples of Levels of Service for Highways, Roads and Streets

Classification	AADT (Veh/Day)	Hours per Day of Snow and Ice Control	Levels of Service
Super Commute	30,000 +	24	All lanes will have substantially bare pavement before coverage time is reduced
Urban Freeway	Regardless of Volume	24	All lanes will have substantially bare pavement before coverage time is reduced
Urban Commuter	10,000 - 30,000	24	All lanes will have substantially bare pavement before coverage time is reduced.
Urban Arterial Street	5,000-30,000	24	All lanes will have substantially bare pavement before coverage time is reduced
Rural Commuter	2,000 – 10,000	20	The right lane on divided roadways and both lanes on two lane roads will have bare wheel paths with intermittent bare pavement before coverage time is reduced. The left lane on divided roadways will have intermittent bare wheel paths with chemically treated or sanded hills and curves.
Urban Collector Street	500-5,000	18	75 % Bare Pavement (St. Louis, MO Co.)
Primary	800 – 2,000	18	Both lanes will have intermittent bare wheel paths with chemically treated or sanded hills and curves before coverage time is reduced.
Urban Residential Street	200-500	12	75 % Bare Pavement (St. Louis, MO Co.)
Secondary	Under 800	12	One wheel path in each lane will have intermittent bare pavement with chemically treated or sanded hills and curves before coverage time is reduced.
Suburban or Rural Residential Street	Under 200	12	75 % Bare Pavement (St. Louis, MO Co.)

For example, the LOS for the Colorado Department of Transportation is twenty-four-hour coverage for roads with more than 2,000 vehicles on average daily, and fourteen-hour coverage for roads with less than 2,000 per day. Determinations of attainment or non-attainment of LOS is based on visual observations of pavement conditions by either operators or supervisors.

Innovation in the Organization

It is important that managers and supervisors at all levels foster a culture of innovation within the organization. The organization, not just individuals, should be receptive to change by evaluating and perhaps implementing new technologies and methods. The organizational culture should proactively seek progressive changes — changes that improve processes, reduce resource expenditures, or both.

Ideally, the organization should possess a commitment to a continuous improvement in the quality of its work. Although top management support is essential for implementation of innovation, the entire organizational structure should be involved in the implementation process. This can be accomplished through periodic meetings of managers, supervisors, and operators, and recognizing and rewarding innovators for efforts to improve the effectiveness and efficiency of the organization. Quality initiatives, such as quality circles and total quality management can assist in solving local problems.

Innovation needs to be encouraged and recognized as a positive way of improving service to the customer. This process will require an acceptance of prudent risk-taking, and the recognition of the potential for occasional failures as the price of progress.

References

1. Jesse Story, FHWA, Presentation at a Minnesota DOT RWIS workshop, December 4, 1995, Minneapolis, MN.

2. Sävenhed, Hans, *Relation Between Winter Road Maintenance And Road Safety,* Report 399A, Swedish National Road and Transport Research Institute, 1995

3. Hanbali, Rashad M. and D. A. Kuemmel. "Traffic Volume Reductions Due to Winter Storm Conditions," *Snow Removal and Ice Control Technology,* TRB Record No. 1387, pages 159-164. Transportation Research Board, Washington, D.C., 1993.

4. Geer, Ira W., ed., *Glossary of Weather and Climate,* American Meteorological Society, 1996.

5. Road Weather Information Systems Volume 1: Research Report (SHRP-H-350). Strategic Highway Research Program, National Research Council, Washington, DC, 1993.

6. *Ice and Snow Removal Manual, Volume 1,* Minnesota Department of Transportation, February 1991.

2 Administration and Management

Communications

Effective communication is the key to the success of any organization. The priority/emergency nature of snow and ice control operations makes communications within and between maintenance organizations, adjacent maintenance providers, other impacted organizations, and the public even more critical.

The magnitude and complexity of communications systems usually depends on the size and resources of the maintenance organization. For example, truck-to-dispatcher/supervisor radio communication and telephone/fax communication between the dispatcher/supervisor and other interested parties may be adequate for a township with limited responsibility. However, an operations center with remote monitoring capability for equipment location, road and weather conditions, video traffic displays, etc., may be a more appropriate communications configuration for a state highway agency or large municipality with significant responsibility.

Internal Communications

Internal communications systems link the entire organization, from the crew level to the CEO. Integration of crew-level communications with supervisory- and management-level communications is vital to the coordination of emergency road operations. Supervisors need to know the locations of road crews, equipment, and current status of various operations in order to provide guidance and direction to crewmembers. Managers generally need to know anticipated weather conditions, progress of crewmembers, approximated cost of operations, significant incidents, road closures, traffic movement problems, and the estimated time to complete various operations. This information is required for management decisions, but can also be valuable to other interested parties, such as emergency managers and the traveling public. Coordination of work at crew or jurisdictional interfaces is also very important. Abrupt changes in the snow and ice level of service can be a hazard to motorists.

For organizations that staff trucks with only one person, crew-level communications are particularly important.   Snow and ice operations are physically demanding, sometimes performed alone in remote areas, and are potentially dangerous. At the crew level, the ability to communicate on matters of public safety, accidents, incidents, work coordination, personal safety, weather conditions, road conditions, and work progress is absolutely vital.

Team Building

Team building and recognition is often forgotten in the communications process. Most snow and ice control personnel exhibit a high level of commitment and knowledge. They should be routinely recognized through formal programs or a simple "well done" from their supervisors. Allowing workers to participate in policy development, planning, equipment acquisition, and work evaluation activities, if done positively, has training and team building value.

External Communications and Customer Considerations

External communications, often overlooked as an aspect of snow and ice control programs, can pay huge dividends in terms of public, political, and media support; public safety; institutional knowledge; operational cost; and operational effectiveness.

Communicating With the Public

Communication with the public is becoming more important as traffic volumes and communication methods increase.   A well-informed public, coupled with customer-friendly service, is key to a successful snow and ice control program. Weather bulletins, press releases, and other public announcements emphasize the road users' responsibility to drive safely and appropriately for the conditions they encounter or can expect.

Effective dealings with the public also include "good neighbor" initiatives. Examples of efforts that can foster good relationships include:

 ❊ *Environmental Issues.* Effective pollution control at facilities is
    a must. Keeping ice control chemicals out of the surrounding
    environment prevents poor public trust and law suits. The

proper collection, treatment, and disposal of wash water, waste oils, engine coolants, and other waste substances are just plain good business practices.

❄ *Outreach.* Open houses and other community outreach programs are effective means to communicate the objectives and limitations of the maintenance programs. Depending upon the agency and community, snowplow competitions or rodeos might be suitable activities for open houses, building public confidence through demonstrations of operations and safety skills while providing valuable internal training. Public information brochures help establish an understanding of the purpose for snow and ice control and set the level of expectation for the winter.

Staff representing the maintenance organization, police, and emergency services agencies are effective outreach teams in communicating safety and policy information. Target audiences include such civic and community groups as automobile clubs (e.g., AAA), Kiwanis, Rotary Club, Veterans of Foreign Wars (VFW), Daughters of the American Revolution (DAR), Lions Club, Parent Teacher Associations (PTA's), churches, schools, volunteer fire organizations, and fraternal organizations. Maintenance organizations that have instituted outreach programs have seen a reduction in the number of service complaints.

❄ *Facility Appearance.* Maintenance facilities that have an acceptable appearance and do not pollute the environment are more likely to be appreciated by neighboring residents and the public. The nature of transportation maintenance requires the storage of equipment, fuel, aggregates, abrasives, ice control chemicals, scrap, waste products, metal, traffic protection devices, and other materials. Areas providing external storage should be kept neat, while scrap and other visually displeasing items should be screened to the extent possible. While there may be few choices in the facility structures, they should be securely fenced, well maintained, and painted. Landscaping can add significantly to the appearance of a facility.

❄ *Driving Schools.* Contacting driver training schools to ask them to emphasize winter driving hazards and techniques as winter approaches is a good means for encouraging safe driving and for appreciating snow and ice control efforts.

Communicating With the Media

Effective communications with the media has high customer service and public-relations value. The media can make or break a maintenance organization's image. By making the media part of the snow and ice control team (as well as construction and maintenance efforts), information on winter road conditions, weather data, and highway operations can be swiftly communicated to the public. Work with the media to convey information on:

❄ snow emergency regulations;

❄ use of studded tires;

❄ tire tread depth regulations;

❄ preparing vehicles for winter;

❄ winter driving techniques;

❄ interacting with snow and ice control equipment;

❄ driveway policy;

❄ sidewalk clearing policy;

❄ damage caused by snow and ice operations (policy);

❄ snow removal policy;

❄ treatment procedures;

❄ priority and policy;

❄ new technology; and

❄ driver responsibility and courtesy.

The media need to understand policies and operations. This can be accomplished through media days, open houses and snow rodeos, pre-season briefings, participation in policy development, and timely communication of accurate weather data, highway conditions and the status of operations. Agency spokespersons should be available to provide information on maintenance activities throughout the year, not just during snow emergencies.

If an operations center is in use, allowing media access to automated real time video data, weather data, traffic data, and pavement data enhances communications. There may be concerns associated with the release of this information, such as having media and road users attempting to interpret data. Nevertheless, a maintenance agency that has a reasonable written policy for responding to the data and makes a good-faith effort to adhere to the policy should experience few legal problems. Periodic, timely, and accurate news releases or bulletins from the operations center by faxing information to a pre-selected phone list or posting it on a web site is another good way to communicate with the media/public.

Communicating, Coordinating, and Cooperating with Customers

Before determining how to communicate, coordinate, and cooperate with the customers of snow and ice control service, an agency should target its constituency and potential clients. A listing may include:

 * commuters;

 * users of school bus, transit and rail systems;

 * emergency services such as medical, fire, and police;

 * neighboring snow and ice service providers;

 * business travelers;

 * trucking companies and shippers (warehouses on wheels);

 * customer-oriented community businesses (health care, manufacturing, emergency and human service providers);

 * motor vehicle insurance industry;

 * inter-jurisdictional travelers;

 * food production industry;

 * recreational travelers;

 * media; and

 * automobile, motorcycle, and trucker clubs and associations.

With this broad a constituency, effective communications is a challenge. A good way to start is to bring representatives of this community into the planning and policy development process. They can also be recipients of the news bulletins, informational brochures, and releases described above.

Customer Input. It is very difficult to obtain input from the traveling public. Market research through questionnaires (oral, phone, e-mail, or written) is sometimes used to elicit public opinion. This is a science within itself and questionnaires should be designed and evaluated by people who are trained in this area. The goal of snow and ice market research and customer representation should be to obtain customer reaction and input relative to costs and benefits, level of service, operational policies, and communication effectiveness. Other market research tools include public hearings, local access cable TV channels, telephone hot lines, and as noted above, community outreach activities. Pre- and post-season meetings with representatives of the various customer groups can also provide valuable input and insights.

Another concept in the customer input process is to have the traveling public be part of the snow and ice control team. Customers can assist by not driving or parking on the roads while snow and ice operations are underway. They can communicate weather conditions, road conditions, requests for service, and complaints through hot lines, Internet web sites, and other similar forums. If these forums are used, it is vitally important to have investigations and follow-up responses to complaints or requests for service. Volunteers to staff phones and assist in other support activities can also be solicited from the public.

Communication with Customers. It is difficult to convey relevant highway and weather information to customers since no single forum will reach everyone. In addition to the media, other viable forums include web sites, customer groups, highway advisory radio, variable message signs, public access television, weather band radio (cooperation with the National Weather Service) and information displays such as computer touch screens or kiosks at rest areas, truck stops, and other establishments along the roadway.

Coordination of Activities. Coordination and cooperation activities range from local operational issues to multi-state corridor issues. At the local level, there needs to be coordination with adjacent maintenance jurisdictions on traffic and level of service issues, weather information, road closures, and available resources. Coordination with public transportation interests helps to ensure sufficient capacity and movement. Coordination with emergency services ensures mobility on priority" routes and access to incidents that may require road treatment.

Command and communication centers in large jurisdictions perform data gathering, analysis, and dissemination tasks. These centers usually have operational representatives from other customer or service organizations to assist in coordination efforts. They also provide information to the media through a variety of communication methods. In smaller jurisdictions, this function may be performed by a dispatcher/supervisor using radio communications with operational forces and telephone/fax communications with other interested parties.

Corridor-based or regional communications centers are being established in many areas. Here, a major highway (such as an interstate) and many parallel and perpendicular roadways throughout a fairly broad area are visualized as a highway transportation system, regardless of political boundaries. The intent is to inform travelers of situations well in advance, manage traffic flow by using alternate routing, and assure that necessary snow and ice control activities are performed in a timely and adequate manner.

Technology Transfer. Agency participation in forums sharing new technology, innovations, operational procedures and management techniques ensures that policies and procedures are as cost-effective job as possible. Maintenance agencies should attempt to participate in forums such as:

❋ American Public Works Association;

❋ National Association of County Engineers;

❋ Local Technical Assistance Program (LTAP) centers;

❋ Transportation Research Board;

❋ American Association of State Highway Transportation Officials;

❋ Circuit Rider Program (Minnesota); and

❋ associations of various local government officials.

Operational Requirements and Policies for Snow and Ice Control

From the snow and ice control perspective, one of the most important things a political entity can do is to have a reasonable, written snow and ice control policy and to adhere to the terms of that policy. As indicated earlier, the development of policy should be a participative process. The policy should also be a "living" document that is reviewed and updated at least annually.

Level of Service

The most important policy issue pertaining to the application of snow and ice control treatments is level of service (LOS). Here, the policy makers have to balance cost, environmental impacts, the safety of the highway users, and the safety of the people performing snow and ice control operations. If that policy is reasonable, and the agency follows that policy to the extent possible, there will be very little successful litigation involving slippery roads or facilities.

Level of service may be defined in a number of ways. The most common method is to define the level of effort and/or the sequence, priority, and type of treatment at various locations for particular storm types. Another common technique is to define level of service in terms of results by evaluating the surface condition of a particular road (bare, a specified level of friction, passable, snow covered, maximum snow accumulation, wheel track bare, plowed, sanded, etc.) at specified times during and after the storms. This method may be less desirable as it usually does not account for the impact of severe weather conditions.

Priority of Treatment

Policy makers have many options to consider when deciding on the priority and type of treatment, including:

* traffic volume;

* functional classification of the street or highway;

* plan and profile characteristics;

* known problem areas;

* school bus routes and schedules;

* transit routes;

* medical, police and fire facilities;

* major sources of traffic at various points in time; and

* storm history and storm type.

The policy must be flexible enough to allow for changing conditions and higher priorities. Weather can change rapidly and unexpectedly; traffic patterns vary over the course of a day and day-to-day; and emergency situations can develop any time, anywhere.

Types of Snow and Ice Events

Depending on the local climate, there may be thousands of types of snow and ice events. In terms of resource requirements, the list is much shorter and more general. We will try to define the important characteristics associated with snow and ice events and how they impact resource requirements and strategy.

Ice content, water content, or density can impact material requirements (type, amount and cycle), plowability, and compactability. Generally, higher density events such as freezing rain and sleet provide the most challenging road conditions. In contrast, cold, light fluffy snow is among the lowest density.

Event intensity is the rate of accumulation of the snow or ice. High-density events with rapidly accumulating precipitation are extremely difficult to deal with. Wind can be a significant contributor to the intensity of an event

Air temperature often influences the character of the snow or ice event and determines the direction of pavement temperature changes. Higher density and higher intensity events usually occur in the warmer temperature range. Pavement temperature will generally track air temperature at a delay of several hours (absent significant radiation, geo-thermal, and to some extent, traffic effects).

Wind direction and speed (natural and traffic generated) has many influences. The most recognized impact is the blowing and drifting of snow. Wind can also mix the air so that "pockets" of cold air, which would cause frost or black ice, do not accumulate. When spreading materials, wind must be taken into consideration so the materials end up where they were intended. Wind can also decrease pavement temperatures more rapidly through evaporative cooling and by slightly accelerating the heat exchange between the pavement and the air.

Traffic volume, speed, and character impact snow and ice control operations. Traffic-generated wind can cool the pavement and displace snow and ice control chemicals and abrasives. The mechanical agitation and impact of tires can help ice control chemicals work more effectively. Small increases in pavement temperature are associated with tire friction and radiation from engine/exhaust systems. Traffic congestion and reduced speed can impact the progress of snow and ice control operations. Point sources of traffic may require some form of priority snow and ice control measures.

Sky and solar radiation can increase pavement temperature to a level well above air temperature. Ice control chemicals work well with warmer pavement temperature. Cold night sky radiation can decrease pavement temperature below air temperature, an important factor when there is potential for frost or icing.

* *Pavement temperature* is arguably the single most important factor in snow and ice control operations. It dictates how well ice control chemicals will work and whether or not snow and ice will bond to the pavement.

* *Moisture sources*, such as lakes, rivers, oceans, cooling towers, industrial steam and vapor discharge, increase the moisture content or relative humidity of local air. Under these conditions, ice will form in the absence of liquid precipitation when pavement or bridge temperature is at or below the freezing point. Larger lakes and oceans can actually generate rain and snow (lake effect storms) if the wind and temperature regimens are right.

* *Cold spots* represent special atmospheric conditions that cause certain road surfaces to freeze or become slippery before other pavement surfaces. For example, in autumn, bridge decks usually cool more quickly than surrounding pavement since the ground temperature warms the adjacent pavements. In the spring, the process reverses and bridges warm more quickly than the surrounding pavements on cold earth. Many bridges have moisture sources associated with them making them susceptible to frost or ice. Low spots where cold air can pool and areas shaded from the sun can also be colder than surrounding areas.

It is important to incorporate these factors into effective strategies. For example:

* At certain times, various locations will require treatment immediately before peak traffic periods to assure traffic safety and operational efficiency.

* In urban areas, during peak flow periods in high volume areas, equipment can become gridlocked in traffic. Treatment is required in advance of these times. Shift changes might also be appropriate at these times if crews can get to work.

* Larger accumulations of snow or ice on the road between treatment cycles require more ice control chemicals to prevent critical dilution and bonding (unless the pavement is very warm).

✳ Cold and moist spots require priority treatment as most drivers are unaware of the potential for heightened slipperiness.

✳ Light powdery snow on a cold pavement or light snow on a warm pavement may require no ice control chemical treatment.

✳ If plowing is unlikely, fewer human and equipment resources need to be used.

✳ In very limited visibility situations (white outs), it may be safer to remove equipment from the road.

Although this list is incomplete, it should provide enough examples to get a general idea of how characteristics associated with snow and ice events can be reflected in strategic and operational policy.

Performance Measures

Snow and ice control is evolving from an art form to an engineering science. The ability to generate, transport, and analyze huge amounts of data has been evolving concurrently. The marriage of the science and data analysis into data-driven, performance-based management opportunities has made snow and ice control operations more efficient and effective. As a result, performance measures are becoming part of many snow and ice control management systems.

Establishing meaningful performance measures for snow and ice control work is a difficult task that must consider weather, traffic, equipment, available snow and ice control materials, budget resources, training, work rules, and overtime compensation. Over time, these items will become more definable and there is no reason not to move toward a performance based system.

One of the most common measures used to establish a performance-based system is the cost to perform various snow and ice control tasks, including:

✳ plowing snow;

✳ spreading abrasives;

✳ spreading ice control chemicals;

✳ patrolling;

✳ spot treatment;

* benching or shelving (removing the top portion of a snow bank alongside a road with a wing plow);

* mechanical (non-chemical) snow and ice removal;

* loading and hauling;

* clearing drainage facilities;

* clearing safety features; and

* thawing culverts.

For similar conditions, the cost of these tasks can be established by unit of accomplishment (lane-kilometer, kilometer, etc.) at the crew level and summarized for various internal jurisdictional levels.

Minnesota Department of Transportation uses a performance index which is computed by dividing the amount of time a pavement is less than 95 percent bare by the duration of a winter event. A high index would indicate poor performance because of little bare pavement over perhaps a short-duration event. Conversely, a low index indicates good performance. For example, ten hours of less than 95 percent bare pavement for a ten-hour event produces and index of 1, while one hour of less than bare pavement for a ten-hour event produces an index of 0.1. Other performance measures examples include:

* accomplishment per unit of time;

* time from end of event to various pavement conditions (bare, wheel track bare, specified friction number, etc.);

* speed of travel in relation to posted speed limit; and

* some index of customer satisfaction.

Once appropriate performance measures for an agency are chosen and implemented, they can be used in a variety of management applications. Performance measures can establish a basis of payment for contract performance of snow and ice tasks. They can also serve as a basis for performance and fiscal comparison between agencies, contractors, contract forces, agency crews, and zones or regions.

Performance Analysis

Performance analysis (storm specific and seasonal) is a valuable management tool used to assure continuous improvement and justify resource investment. This should occur at all levels of a snow and ice control organization (crew to executive management). There are a number of tools and techniques that can assist in developing a performance analysis program.

Accident Analysis

Accidents are a definitive measure of snow and ice control performance. Since accidents are statistically rare occurrences, they are not easy to analyze. Many states have monetary thresholds above which accidents have to be reported, but many snow and ice incidents fall below this threshold and are not reported. Accidents that are reported are usually the most serious and include extensive property damage only (PDO), injury accidents, and involve fatalities.

Snow and ice accident data may be sorted by the pavement surface condition description on the accident report (snow, ice, slush, etc.). Analysis should go beyond this key to see if other factors (drug and alcohol, physical impairment, and other traffic law violations) were involved. Accident analysis is particularly useful when deciding on level of service priorities and evaluating changes in snow and ice control procedures and policy.

After-Action Reports and Performance Analysis

Analysis of resource investment, storm type and duration, and results are useful when evaluating the continuous improvement of work crews and other units, materials application policy, operational response procedures and resource levels. This is a very important management tool, as data can be discussed and analyzed at the crew level, gathered from work locations, and sent up through channels in larger maintenance organizations. The data gathered in this manner are useful in judging the performance of work units, contractors, managers and supervisors.

Management Debriefings

Anyone having a stake in snow and ice control operations should be part of pre-season, post-season and post-storm briefings and debriefings. Participants can include:

* agency field and central office managers;

* police (local municipal, county and state);

* other emergency services such as fire, and emergency medical personnel;

* National Guard;

* contiguous agencies;

* road user groups;

* business community; and

* emergency management personnel.

Strengths, weaknesses, and outcomes can be discussed along with suggestions for improvement. If additional resources are not available, better use of existing resources and cooperative ventures should be explored. The role of all parties in routine and severe incidents should be clearly defined and agencies must follow up these discussions with action. Periodic simulated exercises of emergency actions are helpful in preparing for the real thing.

Public Information

Performance analysis data can be used to provide information to the media and the public. Resource consumption and various performance indicators can be reported periodically and appear in annual reports or seasonal summaries. In this context, it is particularly important that the data be understandable, accurate, and supportable. Any changes in policy and procedures resulting from performance analysis can be shared with the public.

Record Keeping

Management decisions are increasingly based on data and data analysis. In snow and ice control, it is important to continuously record and analyze data on treatment, location, time, road and bridge conditions, weather and storm conditions, materials use, equipment use, personnel use, operational problems, cost, policy breaches (and their reasons), and measures of effectiveness. This is true regardless of contract or in-house crews are performing snow and ice control operations.

The most important document in this process is the trip ticket, the work report, or the duty record that is maintained by individual operators. Most of the data listed above originate on this record. Some automated record keeping capability exists in automatic spreader controllers and GPS/GIS systems, but these are not currently in widespread use. Collecting and managing good data will help accomplish:

* development of snow and ice control plans and policies;

* record of activities for tort liability claims;

* performance monitoring;

* benchmarking procedures; and

* training program development.

Bench Marking

Bench marking is the setting of performance standards, fiscal standards, or goals based on data-driven criteria that are proven, reasonable, and achievable. Defining, in measurable terms, the accomplishments of individuals, crews, groups, external agencies, and contractors who appear to be performing the task well develops the criteria. The same things that make it difficult to establish snow and ice performance measures have be to considered when establishing benchmark goals and standards.

The ability to collect and analyze meaningful data is critical to work management. The routine acquisition and recording of cost and accomplishment data is critical to the success of any management system. There are a variety of proprietary and in-house computer-based work management and work order systems being used. It is best to choose one that adapts well to the particular needs of the user. When the system is operating properly, there are several advantages to this approach, including:

* improved monitoring and evaluations of assignments;

* accomplishment levels that can be set and evaluated;

* determination of the cost of any task or operation;

* performance-based budgets that can be developed and analyzed; and

* identification of the impact of budget shortfalls in real terms.

Factors That Influence Performance

Resource Requirements

Once the desired level of service is determined for the various components of the highway system, the necessary levels of personnel, equipment, and materials can be determined.

Resource Requirements

Requirements for personnel, equipment, and material resources are discussed in detail in chapters 3-5. Additional consideration must be give to ensure that size- and efficiency-appropriate loading equipment is available to load spreaders, work stockpiles, load snow, and clear special areas. Depending on the extent of loading and hauling requirements, snow blowers, large capacity trucks, and possibly melters have to be available as well as additional support equipment, including service trucks, tow trucks, and trailer transporters. Not all of this additional equipment requires additional personnel. Truck drivers can load their own trucks. Loading, hauling, and snow pack removal operations are usually not concurrent with plowing and spreading operations and operators should be available.

Contingency Resource Requirements

The availability of contingency resources to deal with emergency and catastrophic situations is an important consideration. If the responsible agency is large and covers a wide geographic area, in-house resources may be sufficient, as disasters tend to be somewhat local in nature. Additional contingency resources include:

Stand-by or contingency contractors selected in advance on the basis of unit prices for estimated quantities of work or best hourly rates for personnel, materials, equipment, and overhead. The contractor is paid a standby fee and must mobilize for work within a specified period of time.

Emergency Management Offices, administered at the county or sub-area level, already exist in most states to coordinate the distribution of available resources.

Emergency Management Plan should be developed by the agency coordinated annually with emergency management agencies and surrounding transportation agencies. The plan should include, at a minimum, procedures to direct resources; rescue stranded motorists; remove and transport people to shelter and emergency medical services; remove vehicles that are interfering with snow and ice control operations; mobilize all available resources; and close highways. Sufficient details of the emergency plan should be communicated to the road users through the media and informational brochures so that the travelers know what to do if stranded by winter weather.

Cooperative agreements for sharing various resources (emergency and otherwise) are becoming popular. Rental rates or other bases for exchange of services are defined in a written agreement. These agreements present some difficulties due to conflicts in availability, but in a true emergency, logical priority usually prevails.

Contracted Snow and Ice Control

There are a variety of contract options for obtaining resources to perform snow and ice control. The contracts may be with the private sector or other governmental agencies. The choice will depend on economic analysis, political agenda, climatology, level of service requirements, in-house resources, etc. The options for various combinations of in-house and contract work are discussed below.

Mix of In-house and Contractor Forces

A popular strategy for providing snow and ice control in moderate or light snow and ice activity areas is to have sufficient in-house capacity to perform materials spreading and snow plowing for a light snowfall. When moderate to heavy snowfall occurs, private sector contract forces are brought in to supplement the plowing capability.

The contract plowing forces may be integrated with in-house forces (particularly in multiple-plow operations on wider streets and roadways) or assigned to particular plowing routes. If assigned to particular routes, the contract drivers should be thoroughly familiarized with the routes well before winter, and there should be sufficient inspection to make sure that the job is being done in accordance with the terms of the contract. When public sector contractors are used, they are usually given total snow and ice responsibility for a designated area or route. As with private sector contractors, quality assurance should be part of the process.

It is usually difficult to obtain private sector contractors that have proper equipment and materials to perform snow and ice control operations. The contracting agency may have to supply some of the specialty items, including: plow frames, plow hitches, plows, self-powered material spreaders, ground speed spread controls, abrasives, and ice control chemicals.

Generally, contractors do not have access to government communications. Consideration should be given to assigning agency personnel with radios or cellular phones to contractors' crews to report progress and to assist in overall communications.

Fully Contracted Snow and Ice Control

Snow and ice control can be fully contracted through the private sector, other municipalities, in-house employees (contract with union), or a combination of these options. The challenge is to have contracts that adequately define requirements and provide for performance-based payments.

Choosing contracting option(s) should be the result of a comprehensive cost and performance analysis. All agency support activities, additional equipment and facility needs, level of service implications, and impacts on other agency programs should be included in the analysis.

A concept gaining in popularity is allowing agency unions or in-house forces to bid on snow and ice work. Some agencies will award to in-house agency forces if they are within a certain percentage of the low private sector or municipal bid. This procedure brings an element of managed competition to the public service marketplace.

Route Optimization

Route optimization technology has been around for many years in the delivery business and is beginning to gain popularity in the snow and ice control field. Various proprietary and public software programs are available to the snow and ice community.

A key element in route optimization is having work sites and stockpiles in the strategic locations. Partnering with other agencies or jurisdictions within an agency, in terms of materials management and exchange of route responsibilities, is a great way to start. Partnering might initially create problems with materials policies and the ability to deliver an appropriate level of service, but they are not insurmountable.

Routes for spreading and plowing operations have different requirements. Spreading operations can treat a certain number of lane-kilometers much more quickly than plowing operations. This typically requires less equipment. There may also be priority treatment locations for spreading operations that are not the same as priority plowing locations. These factors have to be addressed when performing route optimization studies.

Training Programs

Training programs are discussed in detail in chapter 3. It should be noted that training of contract personnel is just as important as for agency personnel.

Management Information Systems

Good data are crucial to effective snow and ice control management information systems. These systems can generate a variety of analyses that are useful in judging: crew performance, contractor performance, policy, policy breaches, procedures, costs and benefits, and reasonableness of resource expenditure.

Claims and Litigation

The most important factor in successful claim defense is good records. Written records of snow and ice control operations should reflect what was done; operator observations; and Road Weather Information System (RWIS) sensor output of weather and road conditions. Additional information that should be recorded would include weather forecasts, applicable level of service policy, policy breaches and their reasons, and a description of reasonable efforts to cure deficiencies.

Budgeting

"You get what you pay for" is an axiom often heard. This is particularly true in snow and ice control. Good records support resource allocation decisions and budgetary analyses required to determine the equipment, personnel, and materials needed to deliver the level of service chosen by agency.

Due to the inability to predict weather for a winter season, developing accurate budgets for snow and ice control is difficult. Historical costs per lane-kilometer, or the various level of service classifications with adjustments for the current cost of personnel equipment and materials is a common method. The level of funding relative to average conditions has to be chosen and methodology for dealing with budget underruns and overruns should be part of the process.

3 Personnel Training

Acquiring a capable workforce requires the recruitment and training of qualified personnel. Although in some instances the workforce is acquired through a political process, recruitment of qualified personnel, combined with a strong training program, is the best way to build a competent snow and ice control team. One way to ensure an effective and efficient workforce is to require minimum levels of training, education, experience — including a Commercial Drivers License (CDL) at the entry level — to develop and maintain a high quality workforce through comprehensive skill-based training programs. Agencies should work with community colleges or vocational training programs to develop a pool of pre-qualified individuals.

Training Benefits

There are many benefits to having a well-trained snow and ice control workforce, including improved safety, less downtime of equipment, environmental advantages, and cost savings. Snow and ice control equipment operators, the traveling public, roadside users, and roadside property owners all receive safety benefits from having a highly-trained operational workforce. Highly-trained operators make fewer mistakes and errors in judgment than less-trained operators, thus causing fewer accidents and injuries and less damage to roadside features. Operators skilled in defensive driving techniques are more likely to avoid potential accidents, and those trained in the proper use of snow and ice control chemicals, abrasives, and plowing procedures make roads safer for the traveling public.

Operators educated in the proper use of equipment, pre- and post-operational inspections, and equipment maintenance practices ensure that equipment has less downtime and lower overall repair costs. Proper operation results in fewer accidents and less equipment damage while pre- and post-operational inspections identify easily correctable problems before they become big or expensive repairs, thus resulting in lower overall maintenance costs. Timely, routine maintenance on equipment, including proper lubrication, also results in less downtime.

Appropriate training at all organizational levels results in less use of ice control chemicals, abrasives, and motor fuel. Most ice control chemicals have some negative environmental consequence that impact roadside vegetation, groundwater, and surface water. Abrasives result in air quality degradation and siltation of watercourses. Motor-driven equipment impacts the environment through exhaust emissions, crank case emissions, lubricant leakage, and cargo spillage/waste.

A properly trained snow and ice control workforce uses fewer material, equipment, and personnel resources to achieve the appropriate level of service — real cash savings that can help offset the cost of training.

Training Forums and Primary Target Audience

There are many ways to conduct effective training. The selection of an appropriate forum and a target audience is based largely on fiscal resources and training objectives.

Large maintenance organizations can establish comprehensive training programs with full-time trainers, resulting in uniformly trained, highly skilled people who can be deployed in emergency or disaster situations. Full-time trainers can also be used for training other maintenance organizations on a cooperative or for-fee basis. Specific examples of training forums and their primary target audience are presented below.

Snow Schools, Colleges, or Academies (Operators and Crewmembers)

Snow schools, colleges, or academies are comprehensive training forums lasting one to two weeks and generally conducted away from the normal work locations. Such training forums are expensive since they usually involve a large instructor staff and lodging and meals for students must be provided. Generally, class size is small, providing a low student-to-instructors ratio. If resources are limited, the best use of this forum is to train people who in turn provide training at their local work site. Although expensive, it is certainly desirable to send as many people as possible to this type of forum. Because of their benefits, state departments of transportation, e.g., Maryland and Pennsylvania, sponsor snow colleges, sometimes annually. The authors have developed a suggested curriculum for a snow college, included in appendix B-1.

Classroom Training (Operators, Crew Members, Supervisors and Managers)

Classroom training is usually less costly than snow schools because student-to-instructor ratio is generally higher and the training is usually conducted in closer proximity to the home work locations. This arrangement drastically reduces subsistence costs since only the instructors are away from their home location. Typically, classroom training produces a lower level of effectiveness since it is difficult for the trainer to hold student interest and the opportunity for interactive discussion is limited.   Instructors with good presentation skills and knowledge of the subject should be selected to reduce such effects.

To achieve a higher level of uniformity in operations, it is wise for the same instructor(s) to discuss policy and level of service issues at agency-wide classroom snow and ice control sessions. Minnesota and Pennsylvania Departments of Transportation have excellent training programs, resulting in training materials that are useful resources to other agencies. Details are provided in references 1-6.

Mentor Training (Operators, Crew Members, Supervisors and Managers)

In mentoring, senior workers or higher level staff members work one-on-one or in small groups with less experienced people. This arrangement is usually voluntary, although it can be accomplished by assignment. Here, the mentors meet with the protégés on a scheduled basis and discuss a wide range of job-related topics, including the tricks of the trade associated with snow and ice control. This approach can be very effective due to the one-on-one nature of the relationship. Mentors should work from a manual or checklist to assure uniformity in the process.

Peer Training (Operators, Crew Members, and Supervisors)

More experienced workers in the same job classification can train less experienced people. This is an effective process, as peers are perceived to be highly credible, particularly when they come from another work location and are not part of the social structure of the local workplace. This approach also provides a good opportunity for people who have more advanced training to share knowledge. Manuals or checklists should be used to assure uniformity.

On-The-Job Training (Operators and Crew Members)

Learning the job by actually doing it may be the most common and effective training forum. However, inexperienced personnel should be placed under the watchful eye of more experienced staff until some basic level of competence is achieved. Periodic performance evaluation and training should be a continuing process.

Dark Hours Training (Operators and Crew Members)

In locations where snow and ice events are very common, personnel are sometimes assigned to day or night shifts for the snow and ice season. As a result, part of the workforce works during the dark hours when on-highway tasks other than snow and ice control are generally not done, thus providing a unique opportunity for training during those time periods when there is no snow or ice activity. Many of the training forums previously defined may be used at these times as long as they can adapt to a flexible schedule.

There are many training videos — available from technology transfer centers, other agencies, and the private sector — than can be shown and discussed. A listing of Local Technical Assistance Program (LTAP) videos is available on the Internet at *http://iti.acns.nwu.edu/clear/tech/ltap6.html*. Examples of LTAP training video titles are provided in appendix B-6.

Basic skills can also be enhanced through agreements with local cooperative education centers and other schools.

Skill-Based Certification Programs (Operators and Crew Members)

Many maintenance organizations use a skill-based certification system to decide when a contractor or in-house staff member is qualified to perform certain tasks or operate certain equipment. Combinations of training, operational experience, and demonstrated operational competence usually form the basis for certification. Due to the complexity of operating snow and ice equipment, certification of operators should be considered, as well as annual re-certification of operators prior to the winter season.

Dry Runs and Rehearsals (Operators, Crew Members, Supervisors and Managers)

Operators should test-drive their routes prior to actually commencing winter operations. If the operator is new, someone with snow and ice control experience on that route should go along.

Items that should be noted, and even put on a map of the route, include:

* obstacles along the highway (mark them if possible);

* bridges;

* turnaround locations;

* pipes, drainage inlets, box culverts, and cattle guards;

* raised features on or along the highway, including medians, access covers, grates, speed control bumps, curbs, etc.;

* special plowing situations and ways to deal with them;

* low overhead clearance features, including wires that may sag with a snow or ice load (this is particularly important when using spreaders that require the dump body to be raised);

* priority treatment locations;

* locations requiring special attention, such as super elevated horizontal curves and sag potions of vertical curves;

* public telephones in the event of communication failures; and

* safe havens for use during blizzard or whiteout conditions.

Managers and supervisors can also develop and exercise a mock snowstorm to test weather information usage, agency decision-making, and command and control systems before they actually have to be utilized.

Rodeos and Open Houses (Operators and Crew Members)

Conducting rodeos, sometimes called "roadeos," or snowplow competition prior to winter operations has training and awareness value. A field course that will actually be used during snow and ice operations should be used to test operator skills. Skills such as proficiency in pre- and post-operational equipment inspections, the location of plow ends and their height during operation, safety procedures, backing procedures, accuracy of material spread rate, and distribution should be evaluated. Written or oral tests of agency policy, procedures, and safety guidelines may also be part of the competition.

To the extent possible, these competitions should be made interesting by setting them in an open-house environment with other activities to keep participants informal and relaxed. Senior agency staff should attend and elected officials and the media should be invited for awareness and interaction. These competitions can be used to evaluate the agency training program as analysis of the scores in both the field course and test areas will identify training needs and successes.

Storm and Seasonal Debriefings (Operators, Crew Members, Supervisors and Managers)

The use of debriefing sessions as a training tool and a vehicle for continuous improvement is recommended. Such sessions should be conducted in a very positive manner to help implement quickly recommended changes that make sense. Storm-specific debriefings are very helpful in identifying operational problems and solutions. End-of-season debriefings can be used to identify policy issues and potential changes. These post-season debriefings should involve as many of the partners having a stake in snow and ice control as possible, including a cross section of agency people such as police, fire, emergency management, emergency medical, business groups, highway users, snow and ice contractors, and weather forecast providers.

Conferences and Workshops (Supervisors and Managers)

There are numerous conferences and workshops available, but they may involve significant travel and expense. The knowledge and networking opportunities associated with these forums can be well worth the investment. A partial list of potential conference opportunities includes:

* American Public Works Association (APWA) Eastern, Western, and North American Snow Conferences (Annually);

* Transportation Research Board (TRB) Annual Meeting and sponsored conferences;

* Technology Transfer Centers (T^2) training seminars and workshops;

* conferences sponsored by government officials associations, e.g., county or municipal highway superintendents, state highway officials (AASHTO), city maintenance officials, and associations of towns, cities, or counties;

* vendor-sponsored training workshops;

❄ conferences sponsored by environmental groups or councils;

❄ conferences sponsored by International organizations, e.g., World Road Association - PIARC, Pacific RIM Road Organizations; and

❄ university or school sponsored events.

Training Topics

It is essential that training provided to agency members be thorough and appropriate. Training should be provided to both field operational personnel and decision-makers. The following sections provide suggested topics for each group of personnel.

Training Topics for Operators and Crew Members

The following is a partial list of snow and ice control related training topics of interest to equipment operators and crewmembers. Agency guidelines and deficiencies will dictate the priority order of the topics.

❄ agency safety policies;

❄ equipment operation, inspection, and calibration;

❄ defensive driving techniques;

❄ route specific issues;

❄ agency snow and ice control policies and guidelines;

❄ fundamental snow and ice control concepts;

❄ agency equipment operation policies;

❄ environmental concerns and responsibilities;

❄ operators awareness on physical and mental wellness required during snow removal activities;

❄ winter survival in open rural country;

❄ operator family's understanding of hours and demand on an individual on snow removal;

❄ radio and other communications practices;

⁕ legal rights and responsibilities; and

⁕ agency personnel and staffing policies, including drug and alcohol policy.

Training Topics for Managers and Supervisors

The following is a list of potential snow and ice control related training topics of interest to supervisors and managers. Agency guidelines and identified deficiencies will establish the priority order.

⁕ decision-making process (including the use of road and weather information);

⁕ fundamental snow and ice control concepts;

⁕ emergency and disaster management procedures;

⁕ agency equipment operation policies;

⁕ agency personnel management policies;

⁕ agency drug and alcohol policy;

⁕ communications with the public and the media;

⁕ formal incident command training;

⁕ relationships with other agencies; and

⁕ management system and reporting.

Personnel Management Issues

Because few agencies enjoy a surplus of staff, providing and managing sufficient personnel to accomplish timely, effective, and efficient snow and ice control operations is a challenging task. Overall staffing needs depend on the magnitude and character of the highway system, organizational structure, level of service, equipment, operational safety considerations, emergency/disaster/contingency considerations, and sources of personnel for snow and ice control operations. As a result, developing a staffing plan can be an overwhelming task that requires the consideration of many factors.

Magnitude and Character of the Highway System

The more extensive the road system, the more people and equipment it will take to provide a level of service equivalent to that required for a smaller system. The features of the system, such as stop-and-go operations, dead ends, cul-de-sacs, turning lanes, ramps, deadheading, grades, contiguality of the route, and curvature, will ultimately impact production rate and therefore have to be considered.

Organizational Structure

Larger maintenance organizations usually require a higher ratio of manager/supervisor/ technical personnel to operational personnel. The level of privatization utilized by the agency also impacts in-house staff requirements

Agencies in areas receiving few snow or ice events may not choose to staff for operations at the same levels as those of agencies with heavy snow and ice control needs. Staffing becomes a matter of practicality and economics and agencies must be creative in providing high levels of service when such events occur.

Level of Service

All other factors being equal, level of service and cycle time are interrelated. Cycle time depends on the amount of people and equipment available per unit of highway. The shorter the cycle time, the higher the level of service. Level of service must also include materials storage locations and materials handling considerations.

Equipment

Once the level of service is chosen, the amount of equipment required to provide appropriate cycle times can be determined. Sufficient staff to operate the equipment must then be provided.

Operational Safety Considerations

In heavy continuous snowfall areas, if policy states that workers can work no longer than twelve continuous hours without twelve hours of continuous rest, two operators with different non-overlapping shifts must be assigned to each piece of equipment. This arrangement will also allow for continuous operations. In lighter snowfall areas, agencies may elect to assign one operator per piece of equipment, limit continuous duty, and either provide operations during certain time periods only or continuous operations at a reduced level.

Agency safety considerations usually focus on the length of continuous duty/rest periods, the number of people assigned to snow and ice equipment, and materials loading safety policy. Commercial vehicle laws stipulate maximum number hours of operations followed by eight hours of rest. For emergency and snow and ice control purposes, this ruling is often set aside. Some agencies typically have 1.5 operators for each piece of equipment, e.g., twelve operators and eight trucks. If the agency transitioned to two twelve-hours shifts, some equipment would be idle. By maintaining a maximum sixteen-hour shift with an eight-hour rest, as required by agency safety policies in some states in moderate snowfall areas, continuous around-the-clock equipment utilization can be maintained. Figure 2 illustrates this arrangement.

Some agencies provide two individuals per snow and ice control truck as a routine practice or in special circumstances. Also, some agencies choose to have dedicated operators for materials loading equipment. Others require that spreader truck operators load their own trucks. These considerations impact staff requirements.

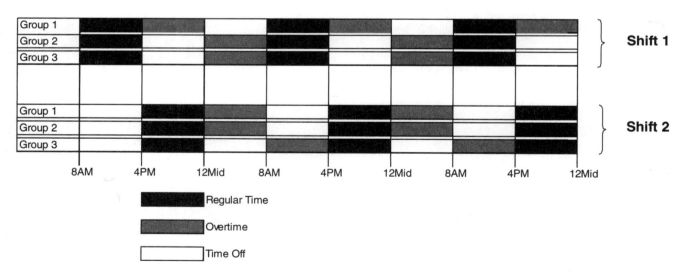

1.5 operators per truck, full fleet operation, with 16 hours on and 8 hours off. Assumes a 4PM full mobilzation.

Figure 2. Time line example for shift development.

Emergency/Disaster/Contingency Considerations

Agencies in areas that frequently experience severe weather year-round sometimes choose to have extra capability to assure timely recovery. This may occur through in-house equipment and staff or a variety of private sector options.

Sources of People to Staff Snow and Ice Control Operations

There are some options for obtaining staff to perform snow and ice control operations. Once the staff is acquired, they must be thoroughly trained for snow and ice operations.

Permanent-Year Round Staff

The number of people required for snow and ice control operations typically exceeds the amount of permanent staff available in most maintenance organizations, though some agencies have sufficient permanent staff. Permanent staff usually works out best, as they are familiar with agency equipment, policy, procedures, and the characteristics of the local highway system. Agencies must estimate additional personnel needs based on the history of the workforce. This includes their experiences with sick and other leave during winter seasons. The agency must also develop a policy for vacation authorization during the winter season in order to ensure sufficient permanent personnel are available to perform the work.

Staff from other Units within the Agency

Depending on the agency, there may be loan staff available for the winter season or for specific snow and ice events, including staff from other departments such as

* sewer;

* water;

* parks and recreation;

* sanitation, recycling and waste centers'

* specialty crews (bridge, guide rail, signs, traffic marking, soil boring, herbicide, trees);

* engineering;

❋ administrative people who have a commercial drivers license;

❋ mechanics (those not needed to repair snow and ice control equipment).

Assigning specific highway sections to groups from these other areas (including supervision) usually works better than integrating them with the permanent staff.

Temporary or Seasonal Employees

Full time personnel can be hired for a specific time period such as the length of the snow and ice season. Temporary staff are usually less costly since they receive fewer employee benefits and are generally paid less salary. When not performing snow and ice activities, they are available to perform other necessary maintenance tasks. Since temporary employees have little or no seniority rights, they can be assigned to less desirable work locations and shifts. This is also a good forum for considering personnel to become part of the permanent workforce.

Part Time or Hourly Employees

Part time employees work on an as-needed basis. Such personnel receive salary and benefits that are lower than permanent staff, seldom qualify to earn overtime pay, and as a result, they are the least costly source of agency staff. Due to the demand for this type of work, such personnel may not always be available for duty and a larger pool of people has to be maintained. These employees are most likely to have the least training unless they are retired permanent staff (a potential source for hourly staff).

Staff from other agencies, temporary or seasonal employees, and part time workers must be fully trained to conduct their designated snow and ice control operations and to understand the snow and ice control command and personnel reporting structures.

Scheduling And Reporting For Duty

Scheduling and reporting performance issues addressed in this section relate to the in-house workforce. For contracted work, these performance issues must be addressed as part of the contract.

Scheduling

Basic arrangements to provide for continuous and non-continuous operations are addressed above. These arrangements usually involve staff ranging from one to two operators per piece of snow and ice equipment. There are a number of variations being used to minimize the inconvenience of shifting, provide timely response, and minimize overtime. These include:

* *Shift-on-demand* is typically used where there are 1.5 or more operators for a piece of snow and ice control equipment. Here, the entire workforce works the day shift in good weather. When snow or ice is expected, half of the workforce is assigned to one of two non-overlapping shifts for the duration of the snow and ice event. When good weather returns, they return to the day shift until the next storm.

* *Staffing every day* is an excellent way to perform non-snow and ice maintenance activities on the lower traffic volume weekends. In this strategy, the operational workforce is shifted (if appropriate) and assigned to each day of the week. Days off are assigned so there will be 5/7 of the operational workforce on regular time duty every day. Staff assigned to the particular workday can probably handle smaller storms. Larger storms will require the use of crew on their normal pass day and/or opposite shift crew regularly assigned to the particular workday.

* *On-demand change* of work schedule is most often used where staffing provides one operator per piece of snow and ice control equipment. When snow or ice is anticipated, workers have their daily work schedule changed to coincide with the storm.

* *Employee fairness* issues also need to be considered when developing general and storm-specific staffing plans. Most labor union contracts stipulate that overtime should be distributed as equally as possible. Schedules should take into account the need to spread pay equitably and to maximize the operational effectiveness. Mealtime considerations during the shift also need to be addressed. For instance, in an urban area, shift changes might best occur during rush hours. Plans can also establish zones of responsibility so that any overtime will be the responsibility of a specified shift or group of workers. It is also important to change the zones of responsibility periodically to ensure equitable distribution of overtime.

Reporting for Duty

Getting off-duty employees to quickly report for duty is critical to providing effective snow and ice control. The techniques used to accomplish this generally fall into the areas of work rules, communications and incentives.

Work Rules

Due to the critical nature of snow and ice control operations, agencies should have a variety of work rules that address maximum time for reporting to duty and stand-by availability.

* *Maximum Time for Reporting to Duty.* Agencies often require that employees report to duty within a certain time period after notification, typically ranging from thirty minutes to one hour. This requirement is usually a consideration when hiring personnel. Housing location restrictions may also be imposed.

* *Stand-by or Availability.* In this situation, workers are ordered to be available for duty within certain time periods. Failure to receive notification and/or report for duty could result in disciplinary action. The Fair Labor Standard Act generally requires some provision of compensation when workers are required to be officially on stand-by, usually if the employee is required to sit by a phone waiting for instructions to report to work. Many agencies use an informal and uncompensated form of stand-by where employees are expected to report for duty when called during certain time periods. However, payment is not justified if an employee wears a pager and can be reached within a metropolitan area.

Communications for Call-Out

Many techniques are used to call employees to duty. Usually, a supervisor or dispatcher calls a list of qualified individuals on the telephone until a sufficient number of workers are acquired to perform the work required. Variations on this method include pagers/beepers where the worker calls back for verification or reports to duty immediately. There are various pyramid methods for contacting workers whereby any one person would contact only a few other individuals. When using these methods, a procedure has to be in place to deal with any breaks in linkage.

Automated call-out procedures are becoming increasingly popular. Here computers do the physical work of notifying employees by telephone — including voice mail and answering devices. A feedback mechanism is usually built in whereby individuals acknowledge receipt of message and indicate that they will report for duty.

Incentives for Responding to Call-Outs

Monetary compensation is a commonly used incentive for call-out response. Agencies may place their employees "on the clock" at the time of the call if they respond to a call out within a prescribed time such as one hour. Some agencies pay bonuses at the end of the season for various levels of response to call-outs. Others provide additional compensation for each call-out response. Reward for competition among work locations, shifts, etc., as incentive for the highest level of call-out response is promoted by still other agencies. The latter, in combination with some type of fiscal compensation, has proven to be very effective.

In the case of assigned standby or on-call duty, fiscal compensation is usually provided even if the worker does not have to report for duty. Similarly, if the stand-by worker is notified and does not report for duty, disciplinary actions usually result.

Compensation

Due to the unscheduled nature of snow and ice events, there are a variety of compensation issues that should be addressed. These issues include overtime or premium pay, minimum payment for call-in, shift pay, or skill-based compensation.

Overtime or Premium Time

It is an almost universal practice to pay 1.5 times or higher the normal hourly rate for hours worked in excess of forty hours per week. Often, overtime worked on holidays and Sundays is paid at an even higher rate. Many agencies do not specifically provide for the payment of overtime to contractors.

Minimum Payment for Call-In

Many employers provide for a minimum payment to employees who are called in to duty, regardless of how long they actually work. A common minimum payment is four hours of regular time pay.

Shift Pay

Workers assigned to shifts that overlap certain time periods are often given additional compensation in the form of bonuses or higher hourly rate. The period from 6 PM to 6 AM is commonly used as a window where additional compensation will be paid.

Skill-Based Compensation

Skill-based pay scales are becoming increasingly popular with transportation maintenance organizations. As a worker becomes more skilled in task performance and equipment operation — with consideration for the complexity of the equipment and accumulated hours of operation — there is opportunity for advancement in title and pay scale. Skill-based pay programs usually involve formal certifications for specific tasks and specific types of equipment.

Uniforms and Gear

Most employers of snow and ice control personnel provide basic safety gear. This includes:

* fire extinguishers,

* hard hats;

* safety vests;

* ear protection;

* flares;

* triangles;

* pad and pencil;

* flashlights;

* leather gloves;

* safety goggles;

* basic tools;

* first-aid kits;

* tow chains;

* tire chains;

❉ window scrapers;

❉ brushes, brooms;

❉ shovels and bars; and

❉ large, clearly labeled and weather protected (e.g., plastic laminated) map of their spreading/plowing route that includes location-specific operational details.

Providing uniforms and laundry service to employees is less common, although some employers provide a special clothing allowance for workers to purchase coveralls, safety shoes/boots, prescription safety eye ware, etc. Some agencies provide winter outerwear such as parkas and overshoes. The intangible benefits of uniforms should be considered, including team participation, individual and group motivation, accountability, and a sense of belonging and identity with recognizable uniforms.

Drug and Alcohol Issues

There should be no tolerance for staff performing snow and ice control operations while under the influence of drugs or alcohol. The Omnibus Transportation Employee Testing Act (OTETA) of 1991 enacted by the federal government is the defining mandate in this area and is applicable to all operators of trucks over 26,000 pounds. This act defines alcohol tolerances, testing requirements, consequences of failing drug or alcohol tests, and confidentiality requirements. Private sector vendors can provide the random selection process and perform the necessary testing. Pooled contracts of smaller employers can help reduce program cost.

Employees who are likely to be in on-call or stand-by status would benefit from special training on the impact of alcohol on their activities before and during their period of availability. Agencies should also have a definitive policy on employee alcohol consumption before and during periods when call-ins are likely.

References

1. "Today's Problems … Tomorrow's Solutions," The Mn/DOT Snow and Ice Workshop cosponsored by the Federal Highway Administration and the Minnesota Center for Transportation Studies, 1996.

2. Equipment Operators Instructor Manual, Pub. 235, Pennsylvania Department of Transportation, Dec 1992.

3. Winter Maintenance Program, Pennsylvania Department of Transportation, January 1996

4. Snow Blower, Pennsylvania Department of Transportation, September 1995.

5. Wing Plow Safety/Awareness, Pennsylvania Department of Transportation, January 1997.

6. Mechanic Orientation, Pennsylvania Department of Transportation, April 1994.

4 Equipment

This chapter addresses mobile and special support equipment for snow and ice control, its acquisition and its maintenance. Equipment and special considerations for materials storage and handling are discussed in chapter 5.

Mobile Snow and Ice Control Equipment

A variety of mobile snow and ice control equipment are used on a routine basis. The most common types, in approximate order of their total numbers, are trucks, plows (front mount, wing, and under-body), material spreaders, wheel loaders, motor graders, snow blowers or rotary plows, sweepers (pick-up and broom), and melters (for melting hauled snow and ice). Each agency determines which types of equipment are appropriate for its needs.

Selecting Snow and Ice Control Equipment

The nature and range of tasks the equipment will be performing and the environment in which it will be operating determine selection of appropriate equipment. In some heavy snowfall locations, snow and ice control operations are the primary function of the equipment. In these cases, the equipment should be designed to perform this difficult function over much of its service life. In lighter snowfall areas, snow and ice control operations may only be incidental to other functions performed by the equipment, such as hauling equipment and personnel for non-snow-and-ice-control highway maintenance activities. The non-snow-and-ice-control activities will drive the design features of the equipment. The key to successful equipment utilization is to balance the design so that even the least common tasks can be accomplished adequately. By choosing multipurpose equipment appropriately, an agency can usually optimize its equipment budget.

The production rate of equipment is an important consideration in the equipment purchasing process as it relates to the overall efficiency of snow and ice control operations. Equipment productivity depends on the system characteristics and the characteristics of the equipment itself. For example, lower weight/horsepower ratio vehicles are less grade sensitive; larger capacity spreading equipment will require less reloading; wider plow paths (the addition of wing plows or using long front plows) will often completely clear a lane in one pass; and smaller, more maneuverable equipment may be more productive in some situations. The range of tasks appropriate to the locale will determine which characteristics are primary considerations in the final selection.

The use of attachments is an excellent way to make equipment more versatile. Front plows, "V" plows, wing plows, under-body plows, and snow blowers can be attached to trucks and motor graders; snow blowers and plows can be attached to wheel loaders; materials spreaders can be attached to truck beds; and a variety of other equipment. Figure 3 shows one configuration of front and wing plows. Effective use of attachments can be achieved through uniformity and ease of the attachment system from vehicle to vehicle.

Figure 3. Truck with materials spreader, front mounted reversible plow and side wing plow.

Specifying Snow and Ice Equipment

Two types of specifications are commonly used to acquire snow and ice equipment — functional and technical. Functional specifications are primarily performance-based, including load-carrying capacity, maximum speed up certain inclines while loaded, stopping distance under various load conditions, and equivalent performance relative to a particular manufacturer and model. This type of specification places liability and responsibility on the manufacturer/supplier.

Technical specifications stipulate particular components of the equipment (e.g., the hydraulic line shall be 3/8 inch inside diameter, constructed of stainless steel, and have a 1000 psi pressure rating). In this case, the purchaser assumes most of the liability and responsibility. Many agencies mix and match between the two specification types to guarantee that they get exactly what they want.

Because of unusual demands placed on snow and ice equipment, particular attention should be given to the items listed in tables 2-10 when specifying these types of equipment:

Table 2. Items to consider when developing specifications for trucks

Hydraulic system	Tires and rims
Gear ratios in transmission	Frame (particularly if using wing plows)
Electrical system	Cold and wet weather operation
Gear ratio in rear end	Engine and transmission
Suspension system	2 or 4-wheel drive (note: 4-wheel drive is costly to acquire and maintain; chains and ballast are much cheaper and almost as effective)
Engine horsepower	
Mirrors (heated) and lighting package for snow plowing	
Quality heaters and defoggers	Power windows
Comfortable, adjustable driver's seat.	

Table 3. Items to consider when developing specifications for wheel loaders.

Reach	Attachment capability
Capacity	Articulation or straight frame
Cold and wet weather operation	Electrical system
2 or 4-wheel drive	Weight and horsepower
Transmission type	

Table 4. Items to consider when developing specifications for material spreaders.

Type - liquid, granular or combination	Ground speed control
Capacity	Spread containment system
Application rate and speed ranges	Pre-wetting capability
Uniformity of application rate & speed ranges	Tie-down/connect/disconnect requirements
Transverse spread pattern capability	Lights & airfoils (if applicable)

Table 5. Items to consider when developing specifications for motor graders.

Cold & wet weather operation	Attachment capability
2 or 4-wheel drive	Electrical system
Weight and horsepower	Transmission type
Articulated to wheel drive	Snow blowers
Truck or loader mounts	

Table 6. Items to consider when developing specifications for plows.

Length	Tripping mechanism
Type (reversible, one way, "V")	Height of wing mount
Hitching mechanism	Vertical and horizontal angle adjustments
Moldboard material, thickness, reinforcing height & geometry [1 (SHRP H-206)]	Cutting edge composition (steel, carbide insert, rubber, etc.)
Shoes (if required)	

Table 7. Items to consider when developing specifications for snow blowers

Production rate	Protection systems
Number of steering axles	Electrical system
Safety systems	Chute configuration(s)
Number of drive axles	

Table 8. Items to consider when developing specifications for snow sweepers.

Capacity (for discharge)	Personnel protection systems
Dump configuration	Pressurized cab, air filtration/conditioning
Operating speed	Sweeping path width
Transmission and drive mechanisms	Broom bristle characteristic
Dust control systems	

Table 9. Items to consider when developing specifications for conveyors.

Capacity	Mobility
Configuration	

Table 10. Items to consider when developing specifications for melters.

Capacity	Environmental considerations related to the discharge system, including separation
Fuel and safety consideration	

Support Systems and Equipment for Snow and Ice Control Operations

A variety of systems and equipment are used to support snow and ice control operations, some of which may not be in general use throughout the snow and ice control community. These systems include voice and data communications, snow fences, equipment facilities, and mobile equipment servicing.

Voice and Data Communication Systems

These systems are used to convey data and voice communications among operating equipment, between operating equipment and base stations, among base stations, between base stations and higher management units and among higher management units.

Radio Systems

Many agencies use dedicated radio systems, as they are relatively inexpensive. Large, sophisticated systems cost $600 to $650 per radio per year (including maintenance). Regular routine maintenance should be part of any radio communications system.

Depending on the area of use and terrain, radio systems may have to be supported by a system of towers and repeaters. Computer programs are available to determine optimum tower/repeater placement in almost any geographical location without extensive field trials.

When acquiring a radio system, it is important to design the power and range for the smallest coverage area possible. The power (output) for base and mobile units should be as low as possible and will depend on FCC requirements and the design characteristics of the local system. It is crucial to have access to frequencies that are unique in the area, otherwise there will be time competition on a random basis and overall poor communication reliability. Any further frequency requirements will depend on the size and complexity of the system.

Mobile radios must be shielded from other operating systems, a process that sometimes requires trial and error. It is a good idea to identify the radio frequency output from other sources when designing and specifying a radio system. This is also true for base or fixed stations.

Many agencies that do not have dedicated radio systems equip their base and mobile units with citizens band (CB) radios. CB radios are not the most efficient arrangement, but do offer some communications capability. FCC rules are unclear if the use of CB radios by government agencies is allowed. If government, especially winter maintenance forces performing snow and ice control, can be defined as a business, the use would be legal. Many state, county, and local governments use CB radios for communications, but their use is subject to certain rules.

Agencies lacking radio communications can establish basic communications with cellular phones. Although pagers are most useful for call-outs, alphanumeric pagers can provide additional operational information. Cellular phones are not as user-friendly as a radio system and they have the same potential for dead spots. Many remote areas do not have cellular or pager service. Coverage (or lack thereof), as well as agency policy will determine their potential use.

GPS and GIS Systems

Global Positioning Systems (GPS) and Geographic Information Systems (GIS) are becoming increasingly popular and affordable. GPS employs a network of satellites and ground receivers to accurately determine positions. GIS is a computer-based system that stores information based on geographical coordinates. GPS and GIS can be combined into a system that provides Automatic Vehicle Locating. There are a number of safety and management benefits associated with knowing the location of snow and ice control equipment while it is in operation, such as:

* ability to locate stationary vehicles, which in the absence of other communications, could indicate a problem;

* reduce the need for communications traffic on radio systems;

* equipment can be more effectively deployed to critical areas;

* better data for public information and inquiries;

* data can be "played back" for analysis;

* problems communicated by equipment operators can be precisely located; and

* reduced opportunity for unauthorized work or other activities.

Additional benefits can be realized by incorporating other data into the GPS data stream. Sensor data can tell how critical equipment systems are performing by monitoring some combination of the following:

* engine temperature

* plow position(s)

* material spread rate and distribution

* lights being used

* exhaust system characteristics

* safety belt engagement

* oil pressure

* voltage/current demand/output

* hydraulic pressure

* air and pavement temperature

* engine braking system use

* equipment loading characteristics

* vehicle speed

* automatic shutdown

* transmission temperature

Computer-based GIS systems are in wide use for identifying assets and physical features within defined geographic areas. They are used in emergency management centers to provide near-real-time situational data and the location and numbers of various types of resources. The GIS systems are used by many highway agencies to pictorially define the location of roadways, gas lines, water lines, sewer lines, guide rail and safety appurtenances, signs, culverts, and maintenance facilities. When combined with GPS data, the GIS systems are very powerful tools.

Before acquiring such high tech systems, a thorough benefit cost analysis should be performed. Other units/divisions within the agency should be informed to see if they might be developing a GIS, since most GIS systems are department-wide in their application. If the decision is to acquire a system, a Request for Proposal (RFP) for purchase or lease is an appropriate step as part of the acquisition process.

Snow Fence

Snow fences can be an economical means of collecting and storing snow and keeping snow off of roadways. Figure 4 shows an example of storage capacity behind a snow fence. There is a wide choice in fence material depending on considerations of cost, weight, aesthetics, performance, and snow load. Most snow fences are constructed of standard, readily available materials. If snow fence installation requirements exceed agency capability, it can easily be outsourced as there is no specialized skill or equipment required.

Although there is good snow fence design guidance available, some agencies use consultants to do site specific designs. Significant agency input is still required due to the value of local observations over time. In some cases, changing the shape of the roadside can help store snow along the road rather than allow it to blow over the road.

Special consideration needs to be given to land requirements for snow fences and the storage of snow behind them, and vehicle access. In some cases, tree lines or unharvested crops such as stands of corn, can provide living snow fences in lieu of constructing snow fences.

Figure 4. Large snow fence showing snow storage capacity.

Facilities for Washing Snow and Ice Equipment

Snow and ice control equipment should be washed frequently to minimize corrosion, improve operating efficiency, and extend its useful life. Washing facilities should be designed to minimize environmental impact. Pressure washers and hot water may be used for effective cleaning and water conservation. Washing equipment may be portable or fixed depending on an agency's overall needs. Electric or internal combustion motors drive high-pressure pumps, and water-heating capability is available on some units. Items such as pressure washers and high-pressure pumps are relatively inexpensive and may be acquired through the procurement process.

Wash-water handling systems usually involve separation systems and underground piping and storage tanks. The facility should be capable of disposing sediment, oil and ice control chemical solutions to meet local environmental requirements. The design and construction of these systems may be accomplished through the contract process. The Pennsylvania Department of Transportation (PADOT) has specifications for developing washing facilities and wastewater effluent disposal systems.

Agencies should also consider sharing of equipment washing facilities with other agencies to minimize costs and adverse environmental consequences. The use of commercial equipment washing facilities, such as truck washing businesses, should be considered since they are responsible for wash water collection and disposal.

Mobile Equipment Servicing and Tow Trucks

Snow and ice control equipment sometimes needs field servicing/repair to maximize up time. If the problem is relatively minor and can be corrected in the field, a mobile field service truck and qualified mechanic will expedite repair and minimize downtime. Repair trucks should be large enough to provide locked tool and parts storage as well as carry larger items like jacks, tires, and rims. The entire function may be outsourced using the contract process. If this function is outsourced, contract documents should give special consideration to response time.

A tow truck capable of removing stuck or disabled vehicles that impede snow and ice control operations, particularly in urban areas, should be identified. Generally, trucks should have appropriate towing capacity and cable and winch capability. Trucks should be stabilized with chocks, tire chains and abrasives. Pulling the vehicles to a cleared area for final hook-up and removal is often required.

Although this service is commonly outsourced, tow trucks may be acquired through the normal equipment procurement processes. Contracts intended specifically for snow and ice control equipment removal situations or for a more comprehensive mobility-oriented highway clearance operation should be pursued. Towing of private vehicles should be performed only if permitted by law.

Special Equipment Maintenance and Fleet Management Requirements

Snow and ice control operations are very demanding on equipment. Cold weather, a corrosive environment, impact loadings, over-loadings, and increased potential for collisions with other vehicles or roadside features are some of the factors that increase equipment stress. As a result, particular attention has to be given to maintaining and repairing mobile snow and ice equipment.

Equipment Maintenance Programs

The routine maintenance schedule recommended by the equipment manufacturer should be regarded as the absolute minimum requirement for mobile snow and ice control equipment. More frequent lubrication and inspection schedules usually result in greater up time. Strategic pre- and post-operational inspections every shift the equipment is used will help identify small problems that, if not corrected, can result in large or expensive repairs. A thorough inspection and repair of equipment, if needed, prior to and after each snow and ice season should be performed. Fuel suited to the climate, such as winter blend diesel fuel for very low temperatures, should be used. In addition, a thorough cleaning, repair welding, repainting and lubricating of equipment is essential at winter's end. Establishing an off-season repair and maintenance program is a good practice.

The value of highly trained, competent mechanics must be emphasized. Acquiring skilled people at the entry level and providing comprehensive training throughout their career is essential for providing a high level of efficiency and effectiveness within the maintenance organization. Training topics should, at a minimum, include hydraulic systems; diesel engines; electrical systems; tires, rims and wheels; suspension systems; plows wings and material spreaders.

Equipment Maintenance Facilities and Resources

The number and type of equipment repair/maintenance facilities to service mobile snow and ice equipment depends primarily on fleet size and geographic distribution. Appropriately equipped repair/maintenance bays (including spare parts and routine maintenance items) and qualified mechanics should be available at work locations having mobile snow and ice equipment. In smaller agencies, only one repair facility may be available and thus will be used to perform most types of repairs and maintenance. In larger, more geographically diverse organizations, there is likely to be central repair facilities to perform more specialized, complex and time consuming repair procedures. Whatever facility arrangement is used, provisions for immediate repair of equipment during operations should be available.

Equipment Storage and Housing Facilities

Snow and ice control equipment operates in a very difficult environment. Most equipment is diesel powered, which does not start very well in cold weather. Storing equipment in heated garages will help cold weather starting. If such storage is not possible, electrical outlets should be provided for engine block heaters to aid in the cold weather starting process. Equipment stored and used outside during winter operations should be brought into a warm location to thaw out. Equipment should be washed as often as possible after usage during snow and ice control operations.

Plows, wings, and spreaders should be stored in a way that they can be quickly and safely attached to trucks. If possible, hopper-type spreaders should be stored in covered racks in an elevated position to allow trucks to back under the spreader. Figure 5 shows one method for storing material hoppers. Front and "V" plows should be stored so they can be driven into and easily attached, and wing plows should be stored in stands and carts that allow easy, safe hook-up.

Maintenance and Repair Systems

Establish a system for identifying, scheduling, and documenting the performance of routine maintenance procedures for any size mobile snow and ice fleet. This system should also track the life-to-date repairs (type, cost, and hours), usage, up time, downtime, and availability for each piece of equipment. With small fleets, this can be done manually on paper. For larger fleets, computer programs are absolutely essential. Agency-created or commercially available software programs are available to perform this function. Examples include OmniFleet's *Fleet Maintenance Management Software* (http://www.omnifleet.com/product_info/), Complete Street's *Equipment Maintenance Management Module* (http://www.cititech.com /index.htm#complete), and *Fleet Maint* from DPSI Corporation (http://www.dpsi-cmms.com/products/).

Assigning Mobile Snow and Ice Equipment

Most snow and ice equipment is distributed on some type of level of service based formula. One measure of level of service, from the equipment perspective, is cycle time. Equipment capacity and production rate impact cycle time. By using cycle time as the formula basis, many agencies distribute equipment based on the number of lane-miles or lane-kilometers per truck for various functional classifications of roadways. As an example, New York State Department of Transportation assigns trucks to their highway classifications as follows:

Figure 5. Hanging hopper for easy mounting.

Table 11. New York DOT assignment of vehicles based on highway classification and lane miles.

Highway Class	Lane Miles per Plow and Spread Truck	Lane Miles per Spread Only Truck
A1 – Expressways, low running speeds	20	45
A2 – Expressways, high running speeds	30	45
B – Major Roads, 200-500 VPH	30	45
C – Minor Roads, < 200 VPH	30	45
D – Minor Roads, very low volume	30	45

By analyzing the fleet's use, availability, up time and downtime, and the use of route optimization studies, fleet reductions and optimization of the fleet size can be accomplished. The Maryland DOT has developed a comprehensive equipment fleet model they are willing to share. Agencies can also partner with other jurisdictional units when possible to yield some fleet reduction. Agreements with adjoining agencies can result in having isolated pieces of roadway being maintained by the adjoining agency.

Acquiring Snow and Ice Equipment

Ways of acquiring new or used snow and ice equipment include non-contract purchases, contract purchases, auctions, military/government surplus, equipment use partnerships, and leasing.

Non-Contract Purchasing

Non-contract purchasing is relatively rare among governmental agencies. However, there may be situations where the cost of the equipment is below contract purchase thresholds, existing contract prices, or is otherwise available for a nominal cost through surplus or auctions. To the extent possible, several quotations for similar equipment should be obtained before purchasing.

Contract Purchasing

Contract purchasing, using a competitive bid process, is the most common method of acquiring snow and ice control equipment. Lower prices are generally associated with higher volumes of equipment. The pooled-agency bidding process for like or similar equipment might increase volume and assure lower prices. A few of the important features of the various bid processes are listed below:

* *Requests for Proposals* (RFP) can be used by an agency to specify important system operating characteristics and other features. The proposer has the freedom to use new and proven technology and offer options the requester may not have considered. As most RFPs are evaluated on a best value basis, the least cost proposal does not have to be chosen.

* In the *turnkey specifications* approach, completely assembled equipment, with all the systems necessary, unless mounted equipment is otherwise available, is specified.

* To assure larger pools of bidders, *competitive specifications* should be crafted to allow as many competent vendors as possible. If an agency chooses to specify particular manufacturers, as many dealers as possible should be allowed to bid. One way to assure that specifications are sufficiently broad is to have a pre-bid meeting with potential suppliers and give the suppliers sufficient opportunity to review the proposed specifications. Exceptions to the specifications should be investigated thoroughly and changes to the final specifications should be made if required.

* *Bid solicitation* documents should be complete in terms of specifications, customer expectations, and payment. Some of the more important criteria include delivery time(s), assembly sequence, assembly timetables, warranties, routine maintenance, penalties, bonuses, latent defect qualifications, price schedules for various quantities, payment terms, delivery time, and format for the bid.

* Depending upon the type of contract, *bid evaluation and award* is based least cost or best value. The apparent low bidders should be thoroughly evaluated for facilities, materials, processes, personnel, and performance history. Prior to award there should be a meeting to thoroughly discuss the bid, clarify any open issues, and assure that all parties understand the contract. Once this process is complete, the contract can be awarded.

* *Preliminary and pilot model inspections* are best done before the unit is painted to allow for easier inspections and

corrections if required. After the preliminary unit is deemed satisfactory, full-scale production can commence. Thorough and uniform final inspections can be made prior to shipment — it is usually easier to correct deficiencies at this point — or after receipt by the owner.

Partnering

Some agencies have relatively little use for specialty equipment like snow blowers and sweepers. In this situation, agencies independently purchase equipment and agree to share, rent, or exchange service with cooperating partners on a pre-determined priority basis. This substantially reduces the individual agency cost for this type of equipment. Partnering opportunities within and among agencies are almost limitless.

Leasing

Although leasing is more of a financing mechanism, it provides an opportunity to acquire equipment with far less up-front investment. The overall cost of leased equipment may be higher than purchased equipment due to finance or interest costs. Leases are particularly attractive when acquiring high-tech electronic equipment that may become obsolete in a short period of time.

Maintenance and other services, and provisions for technical upgrades or equipment replacement cycles at negotiated or fixed prices, can be part of a lease. Leases can be relatively immune to governmental budget processes as they are usually considered to be a contract that cannot be altered.

Use of Rental Equipment and Personnel

Judicious use of rented equipment makes practical and economic sense. In areas where there are few snow and ice events, rental of trucks and loaders may be cost effective, particularly if the agency does not need that type of equipment for other work. The agency may have to supply plows, plow frames, and material spreaders if there is an inadequate rental source for this type of equipment. Infrequently-used equipment is ideal for rental if a supplier is available, although there is not much of a rental market for snow blowers, sweepers, and similar equipment.

Areas having severe winters may yield attractive seasonal markets for items such as motor graders, trucks, and loaders since most earthwork construction is shut down for the winter season. By limiting the rental period to the off-construction season or providing different rental rates for different time periods, rental rates can be kept low.

An increasingly popular strategy is to maintain sufficient agency staff and equipment to handle light snow and ice events and most material spreading needs. However, in more severe situations, strategies ranging from total privatization to total in-house capability may be used. For example, contracted personnel and equipment may be called in and deployed as necessary. Equipment may be rented during extreme storms, or private sector personnel (non-employees) may be hired to run agency equipment. Such equipment operators must have a commercial drivers license.

There are a number of issues to consider in cultivating a competitive marketplace and assuring performance in acquiring temporary equipment and personnel. For example:

* Always maintain some level of in-house capability to limit dependency on the private sector.

* Consider long-term contracts (six to ten years or more) to allow the contractor to purchase and amortize the right kind of equipment. With such long-term contracts, provision for inflationary adjustments should be made.

* Consider providing a contract award payment to compensate contractors for start-up costs such as insurance and amortization of equipment.

* Consider payment for reasonable minimum annual hours, particularly in less winter-severe locations. There are probably some spring non-snow or ice related tasks where the agency can use up minimum hours.

* Be aware of the marketplace and be prepared to provide specialty items such as plows, plow frames, material spreaders, ice control chemicals and abrasives, communications equipment, and standard warning light configurations, as necessary.

* Enforce uniform performance criteria.

* Always require a performance bond.

Contracting Equipment Maintenance, Repair and Service

Many agencies contract all or portions of their equipment maintenance and repair to the private sector or other governmental agencies. Routine fluid changes and lubrication are increasingly being done by the various "quick-lube" vendors. Major repairs are also being contracted to truck and equipment repair centers on a time and materials/parts or flat rate basis, depending on agency needs. Contract provisions should stipulate expeditious repairs during snow or ice events and contractors should be chosen on the basis of a cost and effectiveness analysis.

Economic Analysis of Alternatives

A cost and effectiveness analysis should be the basis for the agency's decision regarding snow and ice control equipment. Keeping good routine cost and effectiveness data will help in making rational and informed decisions. The following data and assessments are useful in performing an economic analysis:

* unit cost for various repair and equipment maintenance tasks (direct regular time labor and materials);

* program area overhead (equipment) costs, including parts and inventory, supervision, management system, overtime, leave, benefits, pension, and social security;

* life cycle ownership costs for various types of equipment (exclusive of financing);

* costs to administer private sector contracts including moving equipment to and from vendors, supervision, contract management, and supplying specialized equipment;

* financing Costs (should be identified in bids);

* level of service (quality and performance) impacts; and

* private sector unit cost.

References

1. Snow Fence Guide, SHRP-W/FR-91-106, Transportation Research Board, October, 1991

2. Highway Maintenance Guidelines, Snow and Ice Control. New York State Department of Transportation, December, 1993.

3. Handbook for Acquisition, Development and Maintenance of the Model Stockpile. Pennsylvania DOT Publication 284, February, 1994.

5 Snow and Ice Control Materials

This chapter provides guidance on three major topics relative to snow and ice control: materials acquisition; storage, handling, and inventory control; and selection and application of materials for various storm conditions. The materials discussed in this chapter include expendable items used in snow and ice control, such as abrasives, chemicals, or a combination of both.

Naturally occurring sand is, perhaps, the most prevalent type of abrasive used during winter maintenance operations. Other materials include stone chips or screenings (artificial sand), ground slag, bottom ash, various ore tailings, and cinders. A wide variety of chemicals are used in snow and ice control operations as well as the same chemicals in different forms, including dry solids, pre-wetted solids, and liquids.

Material Acquisition

The use of chemicals and abrasives for snow and ice control operations represents a major expenditure area for many highway agencies. It was estimated that application of snow and ice control chemicals, including material, labor and associated equipment costs, accounts for nearly one-third of highway winter maintenance expenditures in the United States, totaling approximately $500 million per year.

Expenditures for sand and other abrasives account for more than 10 percent of winter maintenance budgets, excluding the cost of application and clean up. The use of these materials are expensive in terms of damage to the infrastructure and motor vehicles, harmful effects on the natural environment along the roadway, and additional highway cleanup operations. The acquisition of these materials must not be taken lightly. Frequently, abrasives are available locally and are easier to obtain and their acquisition is, perhaps, more straightforward than that of chemicals.

Abrasives

Abrasives are used primarily during snow and ice control operations to improve traction. Such improvement may be short lived and its duration depends on many factors such as storm type, pavement type and condition, and traffic condition.

are usually mixed with salt or other chemicals to prevent stockpiles from freezing, keep truck or hopper loads flowable, and "stick" the abrasives to the snow or ice surface. Abrasives are primarily used for treating snow-packed and icy roads in rural areas. They are also used on all types of roads when pavement temperatures are too low for chemical treatment treatments to be effective. However, abrasives are not snow and ice control chemicals and will neither prevent or destroy the bond between pavement and ice which are the fundamental objectives of anti-icing and deicing efforts.

Specifications

Many highway agencies have established bid specifications for the procurement of abrasives used for snow and ice control. For economic reasons, agencies sometimes use different specifications depending upon conditions and locations. More restrictive specifications are required for areas that have air quality concerns and regulations. Many local highway agencies pattern their abrasive specifications around those used by the state. In addition, many agencies still use "pit run" or passing-a-single-screen (sieve) size to limit initial cost, an option that may not be cost effective in the long run due to the reduced effectiveness, air quality implications, and higher demand for ice control chemicals.

The specifications for abrasive material should contain, as a minimum, the acceptable particle size gradation range. The maximum aggregate size should be limited to 0.5 in (1.3 cm) to reduce damage to motor vehicles and injury to pedestrians. Conversely, particles that pass through a number 50-mesh sieve (< 300 μm) should not be used as abrasives because they do not significantly improve the skid resistance of the surface. Particles passing the 200-mesh sieve (< 75 μm) are even more problematic because they tend to make the abrasive material stick to itself, cause difficulty in handling, require more ice control chemicals for reasonable workability, and can be detrimental to air quality.

Specifications for abrasive materials should also cover the following desirable properties:

❋ resistance to crushing, impact, and grinding by traffic;

❅ angular particle shape to reduce blow-off from the roadway and improve skid resistance;

❅ dark color to absorb heat to aid in ice melting and thereby reducing blow-off; and

❅ maximum limits on "flat" and "elongated" particles.

Cost-Effectiveness Considerations That Influence Specifications

It is important to remember that specifications must satisfy a number of criteria such as production and delivery costs, material supply and demand, effectiveness, and quality. An engineering assessment of each variable should be made to achieve a balance of the constraints. Abrasives are often obtained from local, or at least in-state, sources to minimize delivery costs. This approach is acceptable so long as sacrifices are not made in the effectiveness or quality of the abrasives.

Pre-Season Inventory and Delivery of Abrasives

In late spring of each year, a list of available stockpile locations and quantities of abrasive material needed for the next season should be prepared from inputs received from field supervisors. The maintenance headquarters office processes the requests for next winter's abrasives before forwarding them to a purchasing department. Purchasing proceeds with the advertising and awarding of contracts for those materials requested that satisfy the agency's specifications. Orders can then be placed for the necessary abrasives from an approved listing of successful bid suppliers.

If winter delivery of abrasives is an option, local maintenance supervisors should continually review the abrasives needs of the maintenance forces to ensure that materials required for snow and ice control operations are ordered and delivered in sufficient quantities and at appropriate times to handle anticipated needs. Materials suppliers should be given adequate lead-time for deliveries since suppliers tend to impose high surcharges when rush orders are demanded. Otherwise, a sufficient quantity of abrasives to handle the most difficult winter of record, plus a little more, should be acquired before winter arrives.

Multi-Agency Purchasing Programs

There are advantages and disadvantages of using multiple-agency programs for the purchase of abrasives, including lower purchase costs per unit because of larger orders, reduced shipping costs, and more uniformity of abrasives used in a given area. These advantages are probably realized more by smaller highway agencies such as county, town and city maintenance departments rather than by state maintenance departments.

One disadvantage of a multiple-agency-purchasing program is the need for a common specification, which is sometimes difficult to achieve. As a result, smaller highway agencies might pay a higher purchase price for the abrasives, especially, if they have a less stringent specification than a dominant-purchasing partner does.

Another disadvantage of such a program is that agencies in a purchasing program consume their supply of abrasive material at different rates and one agency might need to reorder replacement supplies before another, thereby minimizing or eliminating the potential cost savings associated with a larger order. These disadvantages would need to be addressed during the negotiations for developing a multi-agency purchasing program.

Chemicals

Anti-icing and deicing are two distinct snow and ice control strategies that make use of chemical freezing-point depressants and differ in their fundamental objective. The objective of anti-icing is to *prevent* the bonding of snow and ice with the pavement surface through timely application of a chemical freezing-point depressant. In contrast, the objective of deicing is to *destroy* the bond between snow and ice and the pavement surface by chemical or physical means, or more likely, a combination of the two. Anti-icing requires about one-fifth the amount of chemical to prevent a bond from forming compared to the amount required to destroy the bond.

Although chemicals have been used for highway deicing since early in this century, their extensive use did not occur until the 1950s, following the introduction of the interstate highway system and the growing dependence on the motor vehicle for transportation. Ice control chemicals are frequently the application of choice because of the simplicity of their use, additional treatment range, and effectiveness.

The most commonly used chemical for snow and ice control has been and still is salt (sodium chloride). Salt is widely used because of its effectiveness at moderate subfreezing temperatures, relatively low-cost, availability, and ease of application in the solid form with current spreader equipment. At pavement temperatures above about 20°F (-7°C), salt is effective for combating ice and light snow and greatly enhances the effectiveness of plowing under heavy snow conditions.

Currently, ten to eighteen million tons of road salt are used each winter in the United States. Environmental concerns have created demands for more controlled use of salt or even total prohibition in some states and communities. These actions have lead to experimentation with alternative chemicals that promise to be less harmful to highway facilities, motor vehicles, and the natural environment.

Highway agencies have been searching for many years for the most cost-effective chemical to use during snow and ice control operations. This quest has generated information pertaining to other chemical compounds with varied physical characteristics. Though multi-faceted, the journey always seems to lead back to a small group of chemicals that pose both advantages and disadvantages. This result is not too surprising when we review some basic chemistry in conjunction with economic considerations.

A chemical that dissolves in water will lower the freezing point of the solution. As more and more of the chemical is added to the water, the freezing point of the solution decreases to a certain level and then begins to increase. The lowest temperature at which the chemical will melt ice (under steady state conditions) is known as the eutectic temperature, and the concentration of the solution at this temperature defines a point of the chemical solution called the eutectic composition. The eutectic temperature needs to be considered when purchasing chemicals to meet the need of the expected pavement temperatures in the local environment.

Many chemicals have been considered and tried for combined snow and ice control with some degree of success. The five chemicals that have been used most commonly for roadway anti-icing and deicing treatments are sodium chloride, calcium chloride, magnesium chloride, calcium magnesium acetate (CMA), and potassium acetate (KA).

Specifications

Highway agencies that use chemicals during their snow and ice control operations should have bid specifications that govern the roadway chemicals they use. The degree of complexity of these specifications will vary depending upon the political and environmental constraints imposed upon the agency.

The specifications used by many highway agencies to purchase roadway chemicals are varied and range from a simple list of requirements to a complex set of guidelines. For dry, solid chemicals, the simplest set of specifications might require the material to satisfy a specified gradation and to have a maximum particle size. The specification might also require a minimum percentage of the active ingredient, a maximum percentage of other chemicals, and to be clean and free of foreign materials and dirt. For hygroscopic solid chemicals, such as calcium chloride, the specifications should require the material to be shipped in moisture proof containers or "super bags."

For liquid chemicals, the simplest set of specifications might require a breakdown of the chemical composition together with a description of the eutectic composition. Another form of specification would require product vendors or manufacturers wishing to submit their product(s) for a pre-approval process before the chemicals can be included on an approved deicer products list for bid considerations. This process requires the vendors to submit samples of the product(s) plus an analysis of the supplied samples that contains information such as:

* corrosion test data from an independent laboratory analysis according to a specified National Association of Corrosion Engineers (NACE) standard or other specified procedure;

* pH (liquid products only);

* analytical results of all constituents for which limits have been set by the specifications;

* specific gravity chart (liquid products only) with correlating weight and freeze point information presented in 1% increments beginning with a five percent solution (specific gravity properties may be provided for several temperatures in the normal storage range);

* detailed specifications including information on the corrosion inhibitor used in the product;

* information on the minimum corrosion control inhibitor concentration percentages and the appropriate laboratory procedures for verifying the concentrations; and

* completed Material Safety Data Sheet (MSDS).

This procurement process is similar to the chemical deicer specifications used by the Pacific Northwest states of Idaho, Montana, Oregon and Washington and provided as appendix C-2. The corrosion tests described in this appendix are only a few examples. Research is ongoing to continually update and refine snow and ice control chemical corrosion tests.

Additional specifications are applied to chemicals that fall into one of eight deicer categories. These categories are:

1. corrosion inhibited liquid magnesium chloride;

2. corrosion inhibited liquid calcium chloride;

3. non-corrosion inhibited liquid calcium magnesium acetate;

4. corrosion inhibited sodium chloride;

5. corrosion inhibited sodium chloride plus 10% magnesium chloride;

6. corrosion inhibited sodium chloride plus 20% magnesium chloride;

7. corrosion inhibited solid calcium magnesium acetate; and

8. non-corrosion inhibited sodium chloride.

The specifications required by the four Pacific Northwest states are more the exception than the rule. These elaborate specifications have been driven primarily by workability, corrosion, and environmental considerations. A more standard specification for salt from the New York Department of Transportation is contained in appendix C-1.

Finally, the Strategic Highway Research Program (SHRP) Report H-332 entitled "Handbook of Test Methods for Evaluating Chemical Deicers" can be used by highway agencies in developing a set of test specifications for evaluating and approving chemicals for snow and ice control. The resultant specifications would fall somewhere between the two approaches discussed above.

Cost-Effectiveness Considerations That Influence Specifications

The cost-effectiveness comments on abrasives also apply for chemicals. Stringent specifications for chemicals certainly carry an associated increase in cost. In some instances, these added costs are necessary to help protect the highway system and the environment in which they operate. Some liquid ice control chemicals, such as gas well brines, may be available at no cost. However, these products may have to be enhanced with additional chemicals. Restrictions should be placed on the amounts of undesirable components.

Pre-Season Inventory and Delivery of Chemicals

Comments made for abrasives on this topic also apply for chemicals. Chemicals should be ordered by mid-summer for late-summer or early fall delivery to provide delivery well in advance of the winter season. Some agencies have a practice of ordering 125 percent of their average winter use. Bids can require suppliers to guarantee delivery of a determined amount, although it is common to guarantee purchase of a minimum amount, e.g., 90 percent of the normal amount. The demand for chemicals, especially salt, places great pressures on the shipping and hauling industry that delivers the material from the production point to the users, particularly after winter begins.

It is extremely important that the inventory of chemicals be monitored closely throughout the winter and orders for replacements should be placed with appropriate lead times (as defined in the contract) so that the inventory will not be depleted during or before storm events. Rush orders for replacements should be avoided, if possible, because such orders often carry premium charges and may require longer-than-anticipated delivery times because of competing demands.

Multi-Agency Purchasing Programs

The same advantages and disadvantages of using multi-agency programs for the purchase of abrasives can also be stated for chemicals. There are economic and environmental advantages for states and/or local agencies to have a common set of specifications for the purchase of chemicals and abrasives, especially if the states involved have similar chemical requirements.

Storing, Handling, and Inventory Monitoring Of Materials

Proper storage, handling, and inventory control of abrasives and chemicals are critical to an efficient snow and ice control operation. This section addresses these three major areas.

Storing of Materials

Storage Location Requirements

The material storage sites in a given maintenance area must be located where there is suitable access off and on the highway for maintenance and material delivery vehicles. Storage sites should be placed at locations that will minimize non-productive travel time by maintenance forces, maximize use by multiple crews, minimize possible environmental damage, and not create a nuisance to adjoining properties. The number of material storage sites for a given roadway system is determined by a number of considerations including:

* maximum cycle time allowed for a spreading operation;

* level of service of the road segments to be treated;

* special treatment features such as bridges, tunnels, and intersections; and

* capacity of the spreaders.

The capacity of the spreaders also determines the geographic distribution of the material storage locations. The number and location of material storage sites need to be reviewed periodically to incorporate new technology, such as anti-icing, into maintenance forces' snow and ice control operations. For example, there is a possibility that the number of storage loading points can be reduced through the use of anti-icing operations. The type of material stored at some locations could be changed through enhanced operations and shared facility agreements with other highway maintenance jurisdictions.

The Salt Institute has developed a handbook that explains many aspects of chemical storage including site selection. The handbook describes six issues that need to be considered in selecting an appropriate storage site: safety, accessibility, legality, tidiness, economics, and drainage. Half of these issues concern the environmental aspects of the sites. The sites should be located to minimize possible environmental damage and not create a nuisance for adjoining properties. Silos and elevated material storage may have to be considered at some of these locations.

The other half of the issues concern the movement of truck traffic, both in and out of the storage sites. The agencies' trucks generate most of this traffic, though some traffic results from large trailer trucks making deliveries of snow and ice control materials. Thus, the truck traffic flow at the entrance to the site and in the vicinity of the stockpiles must be carefully evaluated, monitored, and regulated for safety conflicts. The stockpiles should be located with enough room for the maneuvering of large trailer trucks. Some maintenance agencies have designed their storage sites for rail delivery of bulk snow and ice control materials. At one storage site in Wisconsin, the cost of salt supplies delivered by rail was one-third less than for delivery by truck.

Storage Site Issues

One common issue associated with storage sites is "How much material storage capacity should be provided?" In the United Kingdom and Europe, cities routinely stockpile up to one and one-half times their average annual material usage. In the United States, storage room for at least 100 percent of the estimated average winter requirements is a common recommendation. However, storage capacity in maintenance yards is sometimes limited and the maintenance forces must improvise with what space they have available.

Two types of snow and ice control materials are stored at maintenance facilities: abrasives and chemicals. Chemicals can be in both solid and liquid forms. Abrasives are normally stored in piles while solid chemicals are stored in bags or in bulk (piles). Liquid chemicals are stored in tanks. Storage requirements for abrasives, solid chemicals in bags, solid chemicals in bulk, and liquid chemicals are discussed below.

Abrasives are normally treated with salt to prevent freezing in storage, to maintain flowability in the spreading truck, and as an aid to help keep the material on the road surface when spread. Normally, treated abrasives, or winter sand as it is sometimes called, containing three to five percent salt will provide a free flowing condition for distribution. The salt content of stockpiled winter sand should not exceed ten percent by volume, even in the coldest regions, as salt mixtures with higher percentages are seldom used.

During the winter season, treated winter sand is usually stored outside on an impermeable pad and covered to the extent possible. Leftover winter sand should be relocated to covered storage buildings after the winter season. Bulk chemicals should have the first priority for inside storage. Any winter sand that cannot be stored inside during the summer season should be placed on an impermeable pad and covered with a moisture-proof material.

Solid chemicals should be stored inside a building or under a moisture-proof cover, preferably on an impermeable pad. Figure 6 shows one type of storage building. Chemicals stored in the open pick-up moisture, produce leachate that drains into watercourses and aquifers, and develop an outer crust that has to be wasted or reprocessed.

Solid chemicals shipped in bags should be stored in a dry place, preferably in an enclosed building. Storage for more than one year is not recommended. Storage should be arranged to utilize the older bags first. Outside storage is sometimes permitted, provided the bags are placed on an appropriate surface, covered with a moisture-proof material, and securely fastened down. Care should

Figure 6. Dome building for storing salt.

be taken when storing any hygroscopic chemicals such as calcium chloride because they absorb moisture and corrode unprotected metal surfaces.

Some of the environmental problems associated with solid chemicals have resulted from improper storage of the bulk material. Bulk storage is necessary because highway maintenance agencies need to have enough chemicals to meet anticipated winter needs with contingency. The potential danger from improper bulk chemical stockpiling comes from brine runoff caused by rain and snowmelt in sufficient quantities to harm surface water supplies, aquifers, and vegetation. Housing the material in a structure can minimize this danger.

Many types of barns or silos are in use for solid chemical storage, ranging from a simple roof over the stockpile to a complete building. These facilities may also house the spreader(s) under the same or appended roof. Storage in enclosed buildings is the preferred method.

The Salt Storage Handbook is probably the best resource for planning a storage facility for both bulk and bagged solid chemicals. This handbook explains the various aspects of sizing the facilities, land requirements, construction details, roof requirements, and ventilation needs. The storage building should be designed to meet the following criteria:

* have a permanent roof;

* provide protection from direct precipitation;

* provide adequate space for loading and unloading;

* provide shield from the prevailing wind;

* have an impervious floor that slopes away from the chemical pile and out the building; and

* provide a containment system for any chemically contaminated liquid runoff from the storage site.

Outside storage of bulk chemicals during the winter season is allowed in some states where covered storage is limited. In these cases, the stockpiles should be placed on impervious surfaces and covered with a moisture-proof material. The surface pads should be large enough to store the largest piles and provide sufficient room for loading and unloading operations. The moisture-proof covering should be tied down carefully and the bases sealed to prevent infiltration of wind-driven precipitation and surface water.

The bulk chemical storage requirements described above, if followed, should minimize any potential brine runoff. A containment system should be constructed around the bulk storage facilities if the maintenance agency wants to completely avoid the effects of brine or if a problem exists that cannot be solved by protective coverings. This containment system should be designed to receive all runoff from the stockpile area. After collection, the runoff can be reused for treating abrasives stockpiles or prewetting solid chemicals during snow and ice control operations. The collected runoff can also be disposed of by pumping and hauling to an appropriate waste disposal site. In general, controlling brine run-off is the preferred means for preventing chemical pollution since it is more effective than collection and disposal systems.

The use of liquid chemicals during snow and ice control operations, in general, and specifically during anti-icing operations, has been gaining in popularity in the U.S. since the early-to-mid-90s. This period witnessed an increased awareness of the benefits of using liquid chemicals during anti-icing operations based on the Strategic Highway Research Program (SHRP) and Federal Highway Administration (FHWA) funded research.

The interest by winter maintenance agencies in using liquid chemicals during anti-icing treatments as either a straight liquid or to prewet solids has lead to the addition of liquid chemical storage facilities in many maintenance yards. Some state highway agencies (SHAs) have expanded their commitment to using liquid chemicals by building and installing salt brine and CMA solution production facilities in selected maintenance yards. The production facilities require additional yard space, not to mention the space needed for the extra liquid application equipment and containment systems. The SHAs have found it to be more economical to produce brine on site rather than have it trucked to the storage site as water typically constitutes 75 percent of the brine.

A complete discussion of liquid chemical storage, brine production equipment requirements, and chemical application equipment is given in the FHWA manual of practice for an effective anti-icing program. Some of the storage and production items covered in this reference include the following:

* inside versus outside storage;

* agitation and circulation systems;

* storage tank material;

* containment systems;

* batch and continuous flow production facilities; and

* design items to consider for a brine production facility.

Maintenance forces have used a number of approaches in the mixing of chemicals and abrasives. Sand and salt stockpiles for winter road use are usually mixed with front-end loaders and/ or motor graders. This mixing is done on an asphalt or concrete surface with the intent of getting a uniform mix. Pockets of unmixed chemicals are still common with this method. Another approach, just as marginally successful, relies on the use of front-end loaders to dump alternating loads of sand and salt, or two different types of dry chemicals, into the bed of a spreader truck as it is being readied for snow and ice control operations. This second approach mixes the two ingredients on a volume basis. The densities of the two materials need to be known in order to achieve a desired mix that will be distributed on a weight per unit area basis.

Some SHAs have found they can achieve a more uniform mixture of sand and salt, or even two dry chemicals, by using a hopper blending method. Such a system consists of separate hoppers for each material, a stacking conveyor, and a power drive mechanism. Each material is metered onto the conveyor from its respective hopper and the resultant mix is distributed to a stockpile for later use. This method has successfully produced uniform sand/ salt mixes with as little as three-percent salt. "Outside" conical stockpiles are sometimes created with cranes. This provides reasonably good distribution of the constituent materials, but is a fairly slow and expensive process.

The liquid chemical prewetting techniques and equipment are more sophisticated than that used to mix dry materials. Prewetting can be accomplished by one of three methods. First, a prewetting chemical can be injected into a material stockpile at a specified dosage. Second, a liquid chemical can be sprayed onto a loaded spreader or on the material in the loader bucket as it is being loaded into the spreader. Third, an on-board spray system mounted on the spreader and/or dump body can add a liquid chemical to the dry material at the time of spreading.

Material Handling

It is a good practice to handle snow and ice control material as little as possible. Excessive handling increases the chances of spillage and degradation to take place, for unwanted moisture to be picked up by the material, or for someone to be inadvertently injured. The loading of the spreader trucks should be conducted carefully to minimize spillage of the material on the outside of the truck or the surrounding surface. The road surface under the truck being loaded should be impervious and allow for easy cleanup after truck loading has ceased for a given storm. A containment system should be constructed around the loading area to receive and collect any brine runoff from the loading operations.

The Swiss federal highway office recommends storing salt in silos. The silos enable faster filling of spreaders because they permit several trucks to be filled simultaneously and drivers can load without additional help or equipment. This system also helps alleviate unnecessary spillage of chemicals.

When practical, winter sand should be mixed and placed in the stockpiles prior to the start of winter. Material mixed after this period will potentially contain excessive moisture and present more handling problems than material that is mixed before winter. Swedish research also indicates that abrasives from "aged" stockpiles (where the chemical has a chance to dissolve and coat sand particles) are more effective in terms of friction improvement and treatment longevity.

There are many potential hazards involved in loading material in spreaders. The following general guidelines should be kept in mind when working in the loading area:

* load vehicles on a level surface;

* do not overload trucks;

* load and distribute loads evenly;

* do not drop the material into a truck bed using an elevated loader bucket (figure 7 shows one method of loading materials using an elevated loader platform);

* avoid striking the truck, box, warning lights, or flags with the loader or loader bucket;

* never leave a vehicle idling unattended;

* conform to the law when loading vehicles;

* keep the loader bucket as low as possible all of the time;

* never allow people on the truck body or hopper during the loading process;

* avoid spilling on vehicles;

* clean up after a loading operation; and

* do not leave material hanging on the sides, front, or back of the spreader.

Figure 7. Loading materials into a spreader truck, loader on a raised platform, person on a hinged access platform.

Inventory Monitoring of Materials

The maintenance of accurate and timely records of materials used on the roadway are an absolute necessity for material inventory and control. These records should be entered into a computerized database for analysis to assist in management decisions.

Many highway agencies use a database to keep track of daily material usage by maintenance area. Sample data elements that are recorded include date, route number, amount and type of material used, and stockpile location. Additional elements may include the type of storm event and the amount of precipitation accumulated. The information should, at minimum, be entered into a computerized database on a weekly basis. Some agencies manually record the material usage data while other agencies are moving towards more automated systems using onboard data logging systems. Various systems for estimating materials use are employed, including:

* known loader bucket volume;

* known hopper or truck body volume; and

* counting the drive shaft revolutions of spreader augers or drive shafts and relating that to materials delivered at various gate openings.

Solid chemical/abrasive spreader control systems that provide data logging capabilities needed to keep track of vehicle activity records now are available. These records can be downloaded on a weekly basis from a "smart card" to a personal computer. This approach minimizes human recording errors prevalent with the manually based record systems. The newer spreader control systems are also compatible with global positioning systems (GPS), allowing the spreader activities to be spatially related. This makes it possible to know, within limits, what happened and where it happened. Automated material inventory systems will be used in the not-too-distant future that combine the spreaders' activities through GPS with a geographical information system containing the highway network and material storage locations.

The amount of materials in stockpiles can be estimated by segmenting them into geometric shapes whose volume can be calculated. When estimating the weight of the stockpile, consideration should be given to the increase in the density of the pile that generally occurs over time.

Choosing and Applying Materials for Various Storm Conditions

Almost all highway agency maintenance managers and field personnel are faced with the task of selection and application of appropriate snow and ice control materials for various storm conditions.   Over time, many maintenance agencies have developed general guidelines to address these issues.   These guidelines have been established mainly through trial and error and are generally directed towards deicing operations. Such guidelines should be periodically reviewed and revised in light of the development new information about potential benefits of anti-icing operations. Sufficient evidence has accumulated from two years of SHRP and two years of FHWA anti-icing testing to demonstrate the effectiveness of anti-icing practices.   This section addresses the following six issues:

1.   design of a state-of-the-art winter maintenance program;

2.   guidelines for material and application rate selection;

3.   role and use of abrasive/chemical mixtures;

4.   test and evaluation procedures for comparing materials and application programs;

5.   environmental considerations related to material application; and

6.   economic evaluation of material alternatives.

Design of a State-of-the-Art Winter Maintenance Program

A state-of-the-art winter maintenance program consists of several elements that have varying degrees of importance depending on the size of the operational jurisdiction it covers and the complexity of its road network. Level of service (LOS) and climatic conditions are important elements for all jurisdictions and must be considered in the design of any snow and ice control operation. Both deicing and anti-icing strategies are part of an overall winter maintenance program and, as such, are influenced by both LOS and climatic conditions.

Both deicing and anti-icing can be used to support higher service level objectives. Because deicing is reactionary, it cannot support strict requirements for reasonably safe road conditions during a winter storm. Anti-icing can improve an agency's ability to meet such requirements successfully and efficiently, but the maintenance manager must ensure that the timing of the operations is consistent with the objective of preventing the formation or development of bonded snow and ice. The appropriate timing of the operations requires the use of judgment in making decisions, that available information sources be utilized methodically, and that the operations be anticipatory or prompt in nature. In short, it requires a systematic or engineered approach.

Deicing operations are discussed in chapter 7 while the elements of a systematic anti-icing program are summarized briefly below and discussed in more detail in chapter 8. The supporting tools of an anti-icing program include three toolboxes: operations, decision-making, and personnel. These toolboxes are further broken down according to capabilities, information sources, and procedures that may be available for a given operation.

The operations toolbox for anti-icing includes capabilities for applying solid chemicals, liquid chemicals, or prewetted solid chemicals, and for plowing. The decision-making toolbox includes long- and mid-term weather forecasts; road and road weather information; nowcasting; traffic information; patrols providing information on weather and pavement conditions; and evaluations of treatment effectiveness. Personnel toolbox includes availability of personnel trained in anti-icing practices and use of information sources for decision-making as well as stand-by and call-out procedures.

In the development of an anti-icing program, each toolbox should be viewed as a critical component of a systematic operation or practice. The required elements of the toolboxes will influence program design and will depend upon site, jurisdiction, and agency levels of service, resources, and climatic conditions. The toolboxes and their elements will expand and improve as newer technologies become available and as more effective operational techniques are identified. It will always be important that the maintenance manager select and maintain effective anti-icing program that addresses the areas of operations, decision-making, and personnel.

Guidelines for Material and Application Rate Selection

General guidelines for chemical application rates during anti-icing operations are given in table 12 for six winter weather events. This guidance is extracted from the FHWA *Manual of Practice for an Effective Anti-Icing Program: A Guide for Highway Winter Maintenance Personnel.*

Table 12. Suggested chemical application rates for various weather conditions.

WINTER WEATHER EVENT	APPLICATION RATE
Light snow storm	100 to 200 lb/ lane-mile
	28 to 56 kg/lane-km
Light snow storm with period(s) of moderate or heavy snow	100 to 200 lb/ lane-mile
	28 to 56 kg/lane-km
Moderate or heavy snow storm	100 to 250 lb/ lane-mile
	28 to 70 kg/lane-km
Frost or black ice event	25 to 200 lb/ lane-mile
	7 to 56 kg/lane-km
Freezing rain storm	75 to 400 lb/ lane-mile
	21 to 113 kg/lane-km
Sleet storm	125 to 400 lb/ lane-mile
	35 to 113 kg/lane-km

Table 12 suggests the appropriate maintenance actions required to be taken during an initial or subsequent anti-icing operation. For each event, there is a range of application rates based on pavement temperatures and associated temperature trends. Most of the maintenance actions involve the application of a chemical in either a dry solid, liquid, or prewetted solid form and recommendations are provided for the appropriate chemical form based on storm and pavement conditions. Application rates are given for each chemical form, where appropriate. The application rates are suggested values and should be adjusted, if necessary, to achieve increased effectiveness for local conditions. These recommendations are gleaned from the practical experience of states involved with FHWA Project T&E 28 and is generally consistent with the Salt Institute's "Sensible Salting" guidelines, but with less aggressive application rates.

No distinction is made in these guidelines for the type of chemical used. The recommended application rates could apply equally to four different chemicals: sodium chloride, calcium chloride, magnesium chloride, or potassium acetate. Users of these chemicals can convert the applications to liquid equivalents if the specific gravity and concentration of the solutions are known. Specifying application rates in weight per lane mile is cumbersome because it requires knowing the width of the lane mile in order to compute the amount of chemical applied per surface area. A more definitive measure would be to express the application rate in mass per area, e.g., gm/m^2, although the use of this unit of measure has not become a common practice in the United States as it has in Europe and other countries.

Traffic volumes have not been found to have a consistent or dominant influence on pavement conditions or traction to suggest varying the chemical application rates except in the case of frost and black ice. It is the only category that incorporates traffic as an operational consideration.

These guidelines do not recommend the application of chemicals at pavement temperatures below 15°F (-9°C). The application of a chemical in this temperature range may create a problem by causing a wet pavement surface to which dry snow can adhere and begin to build up.

The guidelines contain low pavement temperature conditions (below 15° F (-9°C)) that may warrant the use of abrasives for only two weather events: frost or black ice and freezing rainstorms. No recommended application rate for abrasive use is given because there is a large variability in practice. Application rates range from 100 to 1,200 lb/lane-mile (28 to 340 kg/lane-km) for state highway agencies, from 100 to 400 lb/lane-mile (28 to 113 kg/lane-km) for county agencies, and from 300 to about 1,000 lb/lane-mile (85 to 280 kg/lane-km) for city public works.

Role and Use of Abrasive/ Chemical Mixtures

Abrasives or a mix of abrasives and chemicals are commonly used for many snow and ice control operations. The sole function of abrasives is to improve traction, which may be short-lived because traffic will rapidly disperse abrasives and additional frozen precipitation will cover the application treatment.

Abrasives are used routinely for treating snow-packed and icy lower-volume roads in rural areas. They are also used on medium- and low-priority roads in many non-rural areas and on all types of roads to improve traction when pavement temperatures are so low that chemical action is slow and abrasive treatments can supplement deicing operations. Abrasives are not ice-control chemicals and, as such, will not support the fundamental objective of either anti-icing or deicing operations.

The advantages and disadvantages of abrasives must be understood. Advantages include low first costs; some immediate, although temporary, increased traction on slippery surfaces; potential usage at low temperatures when some chemicals are ineffective; and visible evidence of road crew actions. Disadvantages of abrasives include frequent reloading due to low distance of coverage per truckload; reapplication required due to traffic and precipitation; adverse effects on cars such as damage to windshields and body finishes; significant cleanup efforts of roads and drainage facilities following storms and the winter season; adverse effects on the air quality through increased airborne particulate matter (PM_{10} problem); and adverse effects on watercourse ecosystems.

The problem resulting from the use of mixtures of abrasives and chemicals is challenging.   The Ontario Ministry of Transport concluded that mixing salt with abrasives above the level needed to prevent stockpile freezing improves neither the abrasive qualities of straight sand nor the deicing qualities of straight salt. In addition, they found the highway sections treated with straight salt required fewer applications than sections treated with salt/abrasives mixtures, while achieving the same level of service.

The FHWA T&E 28 study found that a mixture of abrasives and chemical applied during snowstorms as an anti-icing treatment will be no more effective than the same amount of chemical placed alone. The study findings suggest that the use of abrasives in the mix can be detrimental to the effectiveness of the chemical and that abrasives applications should not be routine operations of an anti-icing program because of the negative attributes associated with its use.

T&E Procedures for Comparing Material and Application Programs

The SHRP Contract H-208 and FHWA Project T&E 28 contained study elements for comparing and evaluating snow and ice control material and associated applications during anti-icing operations. Both of these studies used an experimental design together with a test- and control-section concept. The experimental designs were developed to provide data that would allow the effectiveness of the treatments to be statistically analyzed, differences between the effectiveness of treatments to be quantified, and the conditions under which anti-icing is effective to be established. The test and control section concept was used to help control some of the independent test variables.   These studies should be useful to agencies and personnel interested in conducting similar evaluations.

Another FHWA-sponsored T&E project is currently being performed to determine the advantages of using pre-wetted finely-graded salt during anti-icing operations. The test and control section concept is utilized in this study without heavy dependence upon a statistically based experimental design to reach some qualitative conclusions relative to advantages of prewetted finely graded salt.

Economic Evaluation of Material Alternatives

A number of studies involving an economic evaluation of material alternatives have been conducted. Possibly the most publicized study is the one sponsored by the Transportation Research Board (TRB) that compared salt and CMA usage. This study examined the economic impact of salt usage on motor vehicles, the infrastructure, environment, and drinking water. These factors were compared with the health and environmental effects of CMA and its compatibility with automotive and highway materials. The study concluded that road salt usage will continue to be the predominant highway chemical for many years and indicated the need for continued research aimed at reducing salt use by developing anti-icing technology, improving salt application techniques, and exploring alternatives to salt besides CMA.

Part of the MINSALT project sponsored by the Swedish Ministry of Transport and Communications involved looking at new methods for snow and ice control. Included in this study were economic evaluations of chemical alternatives to salt, such as CMA. The findings of the study relative to CMA usage were similar to those presented in the TRB report.

The NCHRP Synthesis 207 on managing roadway snow and ice control operations includes a discussion on estimating winter maintenance benefits and costs. The discussion covers much of the same information on salt as is covered in the cited TRB report. It details a Nevada DOT sponsored study involving an economic analysis of the following five alternatives for removal of snow and ice from highways in the Lake Tahoe Basin:

1. no change in the use of salt;

2. no chemical use;

3. singular use of CMA;

4. use of salt with state-of-the-art technology; and

5. use of alternative chlorides (magnesium chloride) with state-of-the-art technology.

The study concluded that the costs of the last two alternatives were about equal, but less than the other three alternatives.

Some studies of the effectiveness of anti-icing technology have also included economic evaluations of material alternatives. A Washington DOT study reported that traditional winter maintenance operations using a sand/salt mixture cost about three times as much as anti-icing methods using liquid CMA. A traditional winter maintenance operation using straight sand costs between eleven and fourteen times as much as anti-icing methods using liquid magnesium chloride. Similar findings were also reported by the Oregon DOT (Parker, R., Oregon Department of Transportation, personal communications, February 1995).

The SHRP study on anti-icing technology showed that in comparison to conventional (reactive) snow and ice control operations, anti-icing operations could result in savings of up to 50 percent in chemical usage and at least 74 percent in abrasive usage. The final report from the FHWA T&E 28 project analyzes data on the cost of anti-icing operations provided by five states: California, Nevada, New Hampshire, New York, and Wisconsin. Of the forty test events for which cost date were obtained, only seven showed test section costs equal to or below that for the control section costs. The level of service attained in these test events is not specifically described in the report. The report does provide a framework for evaluating the costs and effectiveness of an anti-icing program using various material alternatives.

Performance and issues related to the use and effects of various snow and ice control chemicals are discussed in seven papers prepared for the Transportation Research Board.

References

1. *Synthesis of Highway Practice 207: Managing Roadway Snow and Ice Control Operations,* National Cooperative Highway Research Program, Transportation Research Board, National Research Council, Washington, D.C., 1994.

2. Perchanok, M., D. Manning, and J. Armstrong, "Highway Deicers: Standards, Practice, and Research in the Province of Ontario," Research and Development Branch, Ontario Ministry of Transport, Downsview, Ontario, Canada, November 1991.

3. "Handbook of Snow: Principles Processes, Management, and Use," Edited by D.M. Gray and D.H. Male, Pergamon Press, 1981, p.589.

4. "The Salt Storage Handbook," Salt Institute, Alexandria, Virginia, 1997.

5. Hale, J., "Proceedings of the Northstar Workshop on Noncorrosive Winter Maintenance," Report No. FHWA/MN/RD-84/03, Federal Highway Administration, Washington, D.C., October 1983.

6. Keep, D., Washington State Department of Transportation, personal communications, January 1997.

7. Chappelow, C., A.D. McElroy, R. Blackburn, D. Darwin, F. de Noyelles, and C. Locke, "Handbook of Test Methods for Evaluating Chemical Deicers," SHRP-H-332, Strategic Highway Research Program, National Research Council, Washington, D.C., 1992.

8. "Strategic Investment in Winter Maintenance," *Roads and Bridges*, Vol. 34, No.12, December 1996, pp. 20-21,39.

9. Blackburn, R., E. McGrane, C. Chapplow, and D. Harwood, "Development of Anti-icing Technology," SHRP-H-385, Strategic Highway Research Program, National Research Council, Washington, D.C., 1994.

10. Ketcham, S., L. David Minsk, and L. Danyuk, "Test and Evaluation Project 28, 'Anti-icing Technology,' Field Evaluation Report," U.S. Army Cold Regions Research and Engineering Laboratory, Hanover, New Hampshire, August 1995.

11. Ketcham, S., L. David Minsk, R. Blackburn, and E. Fleege, "Manual of Practice for an Effective Anti-icing Program: A Guide for Highway Winter Maintenance Personnel," Report No. FHWA-RD-95-202, Federal Highway Administration, Washington, D.C., June 1996.

12. 'Snow and Ice Pooled Fund Cooperative Program (SICOP) Workshop," American Association of State Highway and Transportation Officials, April 7-9,1997, Minneapolis, MN.

13. "SHRP Snow and Ice Control Showcasing and Implementation," Federal Highway Administration Contract No. DTFH61-94-C-00177.

14. *Special Report 235: Highway Deicing: Comparing Salt and Calcium Magnesium Acetate*, Transportation Research Board, National Research Council, Washington, D.C., 1991.

15. Oberg, G., K. Gustafson, and L. Axelson, "More Effective Deicing With Less Salt: Final Report of the MINSALT-Project," VTIrapport 369SA, Linkoping, Sweden, 1991.

16. Dye, D., H. Krug, and D. Keep, *Experiments With Anti-icing: An Interim Report*, paper presented at the 75th Annual Meeting of the Transportation Research Board, January 7-11, 1996, Washington, D.C.

17. *Deicing Chemicals and Snow Control,* Transportation Research Record 1157, Transportation Research Board, National Research Council, Washington, DC, 1988.

6 Weather Information Systems

Introduction

Weather impacts nearly every facet of our lives. Knowing what weather to expect, whether it is normal winter weather, or severe weather as depicted in figure 8, allows us to make decisions to take part or not take part in some activity or perform certain tasks. Personnel responsible for snow and ice control also knows how important weather is in determining what will happen to local roadways, when it will happen, and where it will happen. Good weather information is critical to making timely, effective, and efficient decisions to employ frequently limited, but costly resources.

Although weather conditions can essentially be similar over an entire state, pavement conditions are more likely to vary over much smaller regions due to changes in earth surface or pavement characteristics. Elevation, latitude, sources of moisture, such as lakes, rivers, ponds, streams, and cooling towers, and exposure to the sun all influence pavement conditions under certain weather conditions. Highway characteristics also play a role, especially when considering preferential icing of bridge decks.

Because of this variance in circumstances, accurately determining pavement conditions, even at known problem areas, can be difficult. Weather information systems improve the data gathering process and provide decision makers with more accurate, timely data for managing snow and ice removal. The proper installation and use of weather information systems requires an understanding of how weather effects pavement conditions.

Weather and Pavement Conditions

It is important for snow and ice control practitioners to recognize how certain meteorological variables, such as temperature,

Figure 8. Scene in New York City during the "Blizzard of 1996." Copyright © 1996, Max Ule Advertising & Marketing inc.

humidity or dew point temperature, wind speed and direction, cloud cover (or lack thereof), precipitation type, and the amount of precipitation, can and do influence pavement conditions. Precipitation types, as defined in the *Manual of Practice for an Effective Anti-Icing Program*, are as follows:

* ❄ light snow storm;

* ❄ light snow storm with periods of moderate or heavy snow;

* ❄ moderate or heavy snow storm;

* ❄ frost or black ice;

* ❄ freezing rain storm; and

* ❄ sleet storm.

It should be noted that pavement conditions resulting from each type of precipitation can vary greatly depending on pavement temperature and maintenance treatments. Knowing the existing and forecasted pavement temperature can greatly enhance the ability to determine or anticipate pavement conditions and appropriate treatments.

The bonding of snow or ice to pavement results from the combination of pavement temperatures at or below freezing and insufficient presence of ice control chemicals. If pavement temperatures are above freezing (32°F (0°C)) or chemicals are present in sufficient quantity, snow or sleet can melt on contact with pavement.

Even without precipitation, moisture from the air can condense on pavement and then freeze when pavement temperatures are below 32°F (0°C), producing either frost or black ice. These situations occur when the pavement surface temperature is below the dew point temperature of the air. It is analogous to water condensing on a pitcher of ice water. The presence of ice control chemicals can prevent black ice or frost formation.

Climatology

The averaging of weather over time is climatology. Different geographic areas tend to have different weather patterns, producing different climatologies. Reviewing climatology is helpful in ascertaining those areas more prone to the kinds of weather which result in snow and ice control needs.

Certain road segments or geographic areas particularly prone to adverse pavement conditions. Experienced snow and ice control personnel generally know these problematic locations and it is important to include these people in the process of determining the operational procedures and allocation of resources for snow and ice control. This process includes determining the amount and types of equipment, number of people and call out procedures, the selection of materials to use, the amounts to stockpile, and the distribution of storage facilities. Road climatology is also important for determining the locations of weather and pavement monitoring equipment.

ROAD WEATHER INFORMATION SYSTEMS (RWIS)

Since the early 1970s, instruments have been used to monitor conditions in and around runways at airports to aid in the selection of appropriate snow and ice control measures. In the early 1980s, this technology was introduced to the highway environment. In the late 1980s, the term Road Weather Information Systems (RWIS) was developed. RWIS refers to:

* a set of atmospheric and pavement condition monitoring equipment (sensors);

* data collection and distribution systems for measurements from the sensors;

* equipment for the display and presentation of the measurements;

* forecasts of weather and pavement conditions based partly on the measurements from the sensors; and

* all other weather data available from sources including the National Weather Service (NWS), the Weather Channel, other media, satellite broadcast systems such as Data Transmission Network (DTN), companies such as WSI Inc. and Kavouras, and the Internet.

Enhanced Decision Making

Weather and pavement condition information is useful for making decisions regarding snow and ice control. For instance, understanding the relationship between the current weather conditions and pavement temperature and future conditions can enable appropriate decisions on applying or not applying chemicals, selecting the appropriate chemicals, and determining an application rate.

If pavement temperatures are above freezing and are expected to remain so, usually no chemicals need to be applied. Therefore, in order to make informed decisions, managers and supervisors should use the most current information and forecasts of weather and pavement conditions. Understanding anticipated weather patterns arms the decision-maker with information that provides for proactive rather than reactive decision making. Figure 9 illustrates a twenty-four hour forecast of pavement temperature, which can help decision-makers determine the strategies, if any, required during the period. In the case shown in figure 9, below freezing pavement temperatures were predicted for the early morning hours with an increase anticipated through day due to solar heating of the pavement.

Particular attention should be given to bridge decks due to the potential for icing caused by frigid air cooling the bridge pavement faster than the surrounding road surfaces. During transition periods, like autumn, relatively warm subsurface temperatures can help prevent road surfaces from freezing while bridge decks can cool down due to cold air surrounding the deck surface.

Forecasts of weather and pavement conditions should be tailored for the individual agencies, locations, and their practices and procedures. Such forecasts generally require contracting with value added meteorological services (VAMS). VAMS can provide forecast detail necessary for decision-makers that is not available from media or public forecasting services, such as anticipated pavement temperature, storm and after-storm conditions.

Road Weather Information System Components

The discussion of RWIS in the previous section described system components in general terms. The following section provides more detail for each of the components.

Sensors

Sensors can be divided into two categories: pavement and meteorological. Pavement sensors are generally installed at the pavement surface or are implanted at some depth below the surface. The surface sensors typically measure surface temperature, determine the surface characteristics (wet, dry, frost, frozen), provide a measure of the amount of deicing chemical on the surface, and some give an indication of the ice content of the chemical solution on the surface. Figure 10 shows one type of surface sensor embedded in pavement.

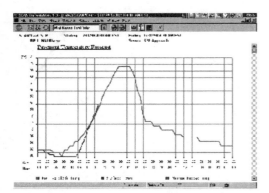

Figure 9. Example of a site-specific forecast of pavement temperature. (Courtesy of SSI®)

Figure 10. Pavement sensor for measuring surface temperature, condition, and salinity. (Courtesy of SSI®)

Pavement temperature can also be measured using hand-held devices such as infrared radiometers, although care needs to be taken to obtain accurate measurements. Recent advances in remote sensing indicate mobile measurements of pavement condition may also be possible. Mobile pavement temperature measurements using truck-mounted sensors are currently available but require the same care and understanding as hand-held devices. Older thermocouple technology still provides an inexpensive short range (readout less than about 1000 ft (300 m) from the sensor) means of measuring pavement temperature.

Subsurface temperature sensors may also be installed sixteen to twenty inches (0.5-0.6 m) beneath the pavement surface. Tracking subsurface temperatures is important for determining whether or not heat will flow to or away from a pavement surface. If the subsurface is warm, it takes longer for a surface to cool. Conversely, if a subsurface is cold, the pavement surface can freeze more rapidly or warm up more slowly.

Meteorological sensors are typically installed within the highway right-of-way to measure atmospheric parameters in the highway environment. Typical measurements include air temperature; relative humidity (for determining dew point temperature); wind speed and direction; occurrence of precipitation; type and amount of precipitation; atmospheric (barometric) pressure; amount of sunlight; and meteorological visibility. Care needs to be taken when installing and using any measuring devices to ensure that the measurements are representative and meaningful. Reports prepared for SHRP provide further details.

Tailored Forecasts

Proactive decision making requires the use of forecasts of weather and pavement conditions. Forecasts of weather conditions can be obtained from a number of sources, either free or for a fee. Free forecasts can be obtained from the National Weather Service and media. These forecasts are intended for the general public, are provided for rather large areas, and tend to be general in nature. For proactive decisions, forecasts must be fitted to the decision-maker's needs, hence the term "tailored forecasts." Tailored forecasts are developed in a consultant-type fashion based on decision-maker parameters and thresholds provided to a forecasting service. Forecasts should be based on the critical thresholds agreed to between the decision-maker and the VAMS. Some forecasting service can also be provided "by exception." If a certain threshold is not to be exceeded, then a forecast may not be needed.

Tailored forecasts are usually obtained by contracting with a value added meteorological service (VAMS). VAMS typically provide a twenty-four hour forecast of pavement temperatures in a graphical format. The forecasts are site-specific and are based on pavement and atmospheric measurements and forecasts for that site although the agency may have to supply pavement measurements. In some cases, pavement temperature forecasts can be provided for road segments rather than specific sites (see below, "Thermal Mapping"). Tailored forecasts should also include forecasts of expected road conditions, type and amount of snow or ice accumulations expected over time, and other weather conditions critical to the decision-maker.

Service from a VAMS should be acquired using a Request for Proposal (RFP) process similar to acquiring other professional services. SHRP H-351 provides an example of such an RFP. *Atmospheric Technology Directory and Buyer's Guide* provides names and addresses of vendors of hardware and services.

Communications

Communications can be separated into two categories: electronic and human. Electronic communication involves the collection and dissemination of data from sensors and tailored forecasts. Sensors are typically connected directly to some form of data logger, usually called a remote processing unit or outstation. Recent advances allow remote collection of sensor data from wireless sensors. Occasionally sensors are sited to take advantage of existing communications or power. This can detract from the utility of the observations, as sites should be selected for their representativeness of specific problem areas or wide general areas.

Data from the data loggers are then transmitted via a combination of telephone, fiber optic, or radio links to a centrally located collection computer, referred to as a central processing unit or instation. Agencies installing RWIS outstations need to work closely with vendors and other nearby communications users to maximize effectiveness and minimize costs.

Additionally, AASHTO, the Institute for Transportation Engineers, and the National Equipment Manufacturing Association (NEMA) jointly established a working group to develop a standard communication protocol for RWIS as part of the National Transportation Communications for ITS Protocol (NTCIP) project. This effort will define an NTCIP Environmental Sensor Station protocol for the Intelligent Transportation System (ITS) community. Although this protocol is in the development stage, agencies should consider language in RWIS requests for proposals that requires successful responders to use standard communication protocols rather than proprietary protocols to ensure competitive bidding and that communication networks are not compromised.

Decision-makers may use remote connections via telephone modem or computer network to access data from the central computer. Field supervisors, managers, and office supervisors can access data via mobile or stationary computer workstations. If central processors are tied to an agency computer network, network terminals can be used. Data can also be distributed and accessed via the Internet.

Display Systems

Vendors of RWIS hardware and tailored forecasts generally provide software packages for use in retrieving and displaying sensor data, weather data, and forecast information. These display packages provide user-friendly access to RWIS information. In many cases, only the information needed by the decision-makers needs to be displayed. The information may also be displayed in a user-selected color-coded display for enhancing the decision process.

Thermal Mapping

Thermal mapping is a process of measuring pavement temperatures over a roadway network in order to create profiles of pavement temperatures under various atmospheric and pavement conditions. The process involves an instrumented vehicle that uses an infrared radiometer and computerized monitoring equipment to measure pavement temperature, distance traveled, and/or the precise geographical location of particular temperature measurements. In some cases, atmospheric measurements are also made. Observations of important topographical features, highway construction features, and roadside features are usually annotated.

Thermal mapping was developed in the United Kingdom in the mid-1980s specifically to address frost or black ice problems. It is usually conducted under varying atmospheric conditions in order to develop representative profiles. This is done because under clear night skies, pavement temperatures can cool more in low-lying areas whereas under cloudy night skies, temperatures tend to decrease with increasing elevation. To be totally effective in the more severe winter areas, profiles should be developed in late fall/early winter, mid-winter, and late winter/early spring.

Thermal mapping has been used for selecting RWIS sites, establishing a basis for forecasting pavement temperature profiles, and for developing optimized plowing and deicing chemical routes based on expected conditions. See SHRP H-350 for discussion of thermal mapping.

Other Selected Topics

RWIS is part of a larger weather information system. Special forecasting software and services plus other available data can complement existing RWIS information and help to provide for more effective decision making. Some areas of the weather information system are listed below.

Acquiring and Using Nowcasting Support

Recent advances in atmospheric monitoring capabilities and refined computer models have allowed the development of nowcasting, the production of short-term forecasts for a variety of weather and pavement conditions in the zero to four-hour range. Many treatment decisions, such as loading spreaders, attaching plows, de-icing, or ceasing activities, are made with the intent that they be executed in this time frame. Sometimes the most cost-effective decision may be to do nothing based upon the information provided by a nowcast.

Nowcasting gives a more precise understanding of what weather, highway, and traffic conditions to expect in this short time frame. The weather component can be provided by exception. For instance, frequent short-term weather forecasts are not needed when weather requiring implementation of snow and ice control procedures is not expected. If a twenty-four hour forecast indicates that weather or pavement conditions that will warrant snow and ice control are expected, nowcasting can be implemented in a time frame to enhance near-term decision-making.

Nowcasting service can be obtained from many providers of weather forecasts. Expect to pay more for nowcasting support than for typical twenty-four hour forecasts (twice a day). These forecasts should be integrated with in-house traffic and resource data to be of maximum value.

Obtaining and Integrating Ancillary Meteorological Data

A number of services are available for obtaining ancillary weather data, such as radar and satellite observations. Some data are available through subscription to services, though in some cases, the same data are available from the Internet. Note that some of the "free" data on the Internet are provided at a significant time delay. Links to weather information can be added relatively easily to agency web pages. Agency personnel and the traveling public can access local weather data readily. Figure 11 shows a composite radar image with precipitation types distinguished between snow (top), mixed precipitation (middles) and rain (bottom right). This image provides an indication the location of precipitation. Observing a sequence (loop) of images will show the movement (speed and direction) of the precipitation.

Observations from surrounding reporting stations will indicate the progress precipitation, temperature patterns, and increases in atmospheric moisture. Each weather pattern provides useful information which, in combination with forecasts and nowcasts, affords the opportunity for making timely decisions for effective and efficient resource decisions.

Many road maintenance agencies are acquiring satellite broadcast dissemination systems that provide near real-time satellite and radar imagery to computer-based display that can be located in any facility as long as there is electricity. The display, sold by DTN and others, can be set to continually update desired images automatically and display them in a looped sequence. The information displayed can be used to time the arrival and departure of storms, and show regional and local variations in storm conditions. The storm and precipitation coverage is limited to standard radar coverage that is limited in some areas. These systems can also be programmed to receive RWIS data from roadside stations.

Figure 11. Radar image differentiating precipitation types. (Courtesy of WSI)

Internet technology permits RWIS data to be stored and accessed from a single server so that it can be shared between agencies. Users can obtain the latest information via local Intranets or via the Internet. Utah and Maryland, for example, have RWIS data on the Internet. Data from adjoining jurisdictions, important for monitoring storm progression, can be made available to anyone with Internet access.

Sharing Weather Information with the Public

Any weather information acquired by an agency can theoretically be shared with road users. In Europe, data from RWIS sites and ancillary data are made available via the Internet. Although most people are aware of windsocks to advise motorists of wind conditions, wind sensors connected to variable message signs can act as visibility sensors to warn motorists. Some agencies are experimenting with ice warning signs using RWIS pavement sensors. Some agencies make NOAA Weather Radio broadcasts available in rest areas, while others are installing DTN and similar systems in order to provide motorists weather information. Ideally, forecasts of road conditions over a period of time would be provided motorists through such systems.

Use of In-Vehicle Pavement Temperature Monitoring Equipment

The desire to know more about pavement temperatures has prompted the development of sensing equipment for use on snow and ice control vehicles. Infrared radiometers mounted on the outside of a vehicle display sensor readings of pavement temperature. Hand-held radiometers are also in wide use for measuring pavement temperature. While similar to thermal mapping, radiometers only provide real-time measurement of pavement temperature at a specific location while thermal mapping creates profiles of pavement temperature over roadway segments. Pavement temperature data are integrated with other location, climate, and geographic data.

Mobile pavement temperature measurements should be used carefully, as the opportunity for error in such readings is great. Errors can occur when the sensor is not pointed directly at the pavement, when pavement characteristics change, and when solar radiation reflects into the sensor. A discussion of the potential errors is provided in SHRP H-350. Hand held radiometers should be stowed outside a vehicle in a trunk or bed to eliminate the potential for thermal shock when an instrument is removed from a cab warm environment to a very cold outside environment.

Both in-vehicle and hand-held devices can be calibrated using calibrated RWIS pavement temperature sensors. The vehicle sensor should be pointed directly toward an existing pavement sensor during early morning hours before sunrise to eliminate solar influence. At least three checks are made: with cloud cover; without cloud cover; and wet surface, but not snow covered.

Archiving Site-Specific Weather Data and Information

RWIS data provide observations of weather and pavement valuable for decision making. However, these observations serve other purposes, such as:

* winter storm reconstruction and post analysis;

* development of training exercises;

* reconstruction of events for legal purposes;

* development of a road climatology; and

* assistance in developing better forecasts.

Because of their usefulness, RWIS site-specific data and information (including both sensor measurements and forecasts) should be archived. A representative surface sensor should be selected for each site. A vendor-provided backup device or diskettes should be used to archive data and copies of forecasts and logs of maintenance activities should be retained.

References

1. Ketcham, S., L. David Minsk, R. Blackburn, and E. Fleege, "Manual of Practice for an Effective Anti-icing Program: A Guide for Highway Winter Maintenance Personnel," Report No. FHWA-RD-95-202, Federal Highway Administration, Washington, D.C., June 1996.

2. Road Weather Information Systems Volume 1: Research Report (SHRP-H-350). Strategic Highway Research Program, National Research Council, Washington, DC, 1993.

3. Road Weather Information Systems Volume 2: Implementation Guide (SHRP-H-351). Strategic Highway Research Program, National Research Council, Washington, DC, 1993.

4. *Atmospheric Technology Directory and Buyer's Guide*, Meteoquest, P.O. Box 10360, Bedford, NH, 1997.

7 Operations

Pre-Winter Preparation

Planning and preparing for winter operations, if done properly, will make snow and ice control efforts more efficient and effective. When preparing for winter operations, the following items should be complete before the onset of winter weather.

* *Specifying and Ordering Materials.* Having access to sufficient snow and ice control materials throughout the winter season is critical. This may be accomplished through a combination of timely delivery and storage. It is absolutely essential that contracts be in place at least a month before the first expected winter weather.

* *Calibration of Material Spreaders.* All material spreaders should be calibrated prior to winter operations or whenever there has been a repair to any of the control, drive, or hydraulic components. The procedure is system specific. Automatic systems are calibrated by running the spreader at several operating speeds and gate openings and collecting discharged material over a specific time period or area. Newer self-calibrating systems should be spot checked by using a similar procedure. (See appendix B-4 for sample calibration procedures). Checking calibration on the self-calibrating microprocessor control systems will require the jacking and blocking of the drive wheels off the ground and the chocking of the non-drive wheels. Keep people well away from the truck while using this procedure.

* *Training and Operator Certification.* The training and operator certification programs described in chapter 3 should be substantially complete before winter operations commence.

* *Equipment Readiness Programs.* The pre-season maintenance programs should be completed at least a month before the first

anticipated event. A system for weekly reporting of fleet readiness should also be in place and activated approximately one month before the first anticipated event.

❊ *Operational Policies.* The operational policies described in chapter 2 should be established well before winter.

❊ *Policy, Regulation, Operational Plan, and Level of Service Reviews.* Review all documentation well in advance of winter and immediately following each winter when relevant problems are fresh in everyone's minds. Any traffic control regulations (parking, routing, traction control devices, abandoned vehicles) should be reviewed and modified as appropriate. Areas requiring special treatment should be reviewed and updated as necessary. Examples of such areas are hills, curves and intersections; schools, hospitals, and major employers; bridge decks and roadway cold spots; transit and school bus routes; high traffic volume facilities; and railroad grade crossings, if warranted.

❊ *Road Closure.* The criteria and procedure for road closures should be reviewed and re-established periodically.

❊ *Route Planning.* Once the operational policies are established, route planning for various operations and levels of response can be done. Plow operators should do dry runs on the route(s) they will be likely to work, and should take particular note of obstacles, narrowings, and other problem and special treatment areas.

❊ *Road and Weather Information Systems.* Any system of instrumentation that provides road and weather data should receive specified maintenance and calibration prior to the onset of winter weather. Contract forecasters and other sources of weather data should tested to ensure communications systems are functioning properly. Any system upgrades or additions should be in place well before winter to allow for normal shakedown and calibration.

❊ *Contract Services.* Contracts for service should be in place well before the snow and ice season. These contracts should contain provisions for operational readiness, communications procedures, and route familiarity. A sample contract for snow and ice control services is shown in appendix B-2.

❊ *Equipment and Crew Assignments.* Necessary modification and re-deployment of snow and ice equipment should be accomplished. Personnel that are required to change work location and/or duty hours should have ample notification and those changes should occur in a timely fashion. Call-out lists, hours of stand-by responsibility, and procedures need to be in place and practiced if possible. All actions must be consistent with labor agreements and/or agency policy.

❄ *Erection of Passive Snow Control Devices and Winter Signage.* Snow fence and temporary snow containment devices on structures should be installed early. Signage for snow emergency routes, winter parking, potentially icy spots (bridges, high moisture locations, shaded areas, and low spots), usual road closure locations, and other notifications need to be inspected and erected as necessary.

❄ *Self-Help Deicing Systems.* Self-help containers, materials, and tools should be distributed to select problem locations, such as stopping locations on upward grades and problem intersections. Self-help tools and materials, when properly placed, can help motorists gain traction in locations where maintenance personnel are unable to provide frequent applications to improve traction.

❄ *Automated De-icing Systems.* Some agencies are installing automated deicing systems, such as bridge deck sprayers that apply liquid ice control chemicals. Such automated deicing systems should be checked for functionality and material supply.

❄ *Drainage Facilities.* Drainage facilities should be cleaned, especially of leaves, prior to snow and ice. Adequate drainage is necessary to accommodate under-snow water and snowmelt, and to help minimize backup on streets and highways.

❄ *Cooperative Agreements.* Inter-agency agreements for mutual-aid, emergency response, cooperative equipment and facilities, and responsibility exchange should be in place prior to winter operations.

❄ *Snow Markers.* Sufficiently tall markers should be in place to identify the location of guardrail ends, isolated curbs, culvert headwalls, traffic channelization devices, hydrants, and other features that could be hit by snowplows. Drainage features should be identified with snow markers or pavement markings. Markers that provide general shoulder delineation should be provided in order to assist plow operators in heavy snowfall situations. Utility cuts, street plates, or other road/street closure/traffic control devices should be identified and tracked on a periodically updated list.

❋ *Media and Communications with the Public.* The media should be briefed on winter operations prior to winter. Communication with customers (brochures, public service announcements, web sites) should also start at least a month prior to the expected first snowfall. Appendix B-3 provides examples of such communications.

❋ *Operational Communication Systems.* Operational communications are work control systems that involve dispatchers, cooperative notification systems such as police and fire, operations center, road patrols, and automated systems such as (RWIS). These systems should be tested prior to winter.

Storm Management

Storm management in the snow and ice control context is a bit of a misnomer. We cannot manage what a storm does — we manage our operational activities in response to the storm with respect to what is predicted, what is occurring, and after-the-storm conditions. The following activities are crucial to effective snow and ice control programs.

Storm Monitoring, Operational Preparations and Operational Action

Accurate weather forecasting and nowcasting, as discussed in chapters 6 and 8, are vital to successful snow and ice control operations. Knowing the nature, time of arrival and departure of the storm, post-storm conditions, and area of impact allows managers to plan and judiciously use available snow and ice control resources. This information can be acquired from several sources including Intelligent Transportation System (ITS) traffic monitoring sites, road and weather information systems (RWIS), weather forecasters, road patrols, and upstream weather reporting locations. Storm information can also be integrated with various ITS features, such as variable message signs, kiosks, and web sites to warn motorists and suggest alternate routing.

Knowledge of storm and traffic patterns allows managers to decide on the type and timing of treatments, the re-deployment of resources if the storm is localized, or for calling in reserves or contract forces if the storm is more widespread and/or severe.

Coordinating Plowing and Spreading Activities

Coordinating plowing and spreading operations is a challenge, particularly if performed independently. The first treatment for most storms is to spread an ice-control chemical to prevent snow or ice from bonding to the pavement (anti-icing). It is important not to plow before the chemical has an opportunity to work. As the storm and storm-fighting efforts continue, there are usually cycles of plowing followed by the spreading of materials. If the plow trucks have spreaders and they are plowing and spreading simultaneously, they should limit material spreading to the freshly plowed areas of the road. If spreading is performed independent of plowing, for example by a different agency, it should be immediately preceded by plowing operations in order to prevent the chemicals from being plowed off the pavement prematurely.

Personnel and Equipment Deployment

Concentrating resources where storm and road conditions are worst is a relatively new concept made possible by improved weather forecasting, nowcasting, and communications systems. Improved management practices for making larger organizations seamless in responsibility and partnering with other maintenance organizations have also contributed to the success of this concept. Concentrating resources is normally used in locally severe storms when local forces cannot meet their LOS goals.

Plowing Procedures

There are a variety of plowing procedures that address issues of wind, highway geometry, traffic, windrows on the highway, snow banks, and snow storage. Figures 12-14 illustrate several variations in plowing techniques.

Multi-Lane Highways

Managing windrows on the pavement, snow storage, and wind are critical issues in the plowing of multilane highways that are influenced by available plowing resources. One approach, sometimes considered the best, for plowing multi-lane highways utilizes a sufficient number of plows operating in close echelon so that traffic can not pass, thereby clearing the highway (and sometimes shoulders) in one operation. This approach has the benefits of not creating windrows on the highway and keeping traffic at a controlled speed in a freshly plowed/treated area where motorists are less likely to lose control. When plowing all the snow

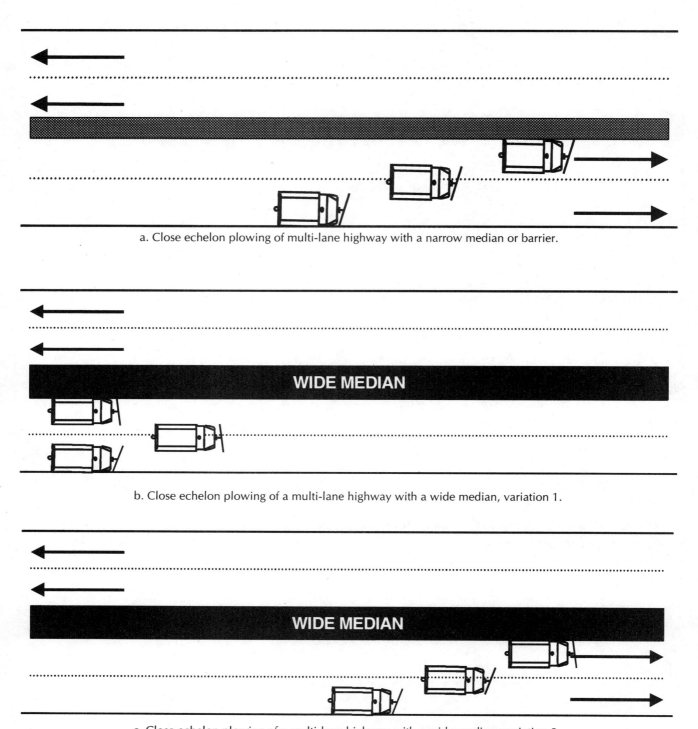

a. Close echelon plowing of multi-lane highway with a narrow median or barrier.

b. Close echelon plowing of a multi-lane highway with a wide median, variation 1.

c. Close echelon plowing of a multi-lane highway with a wide median, variation 2.

Figure 12. Examples of Close Echelon Plowing Patterns.

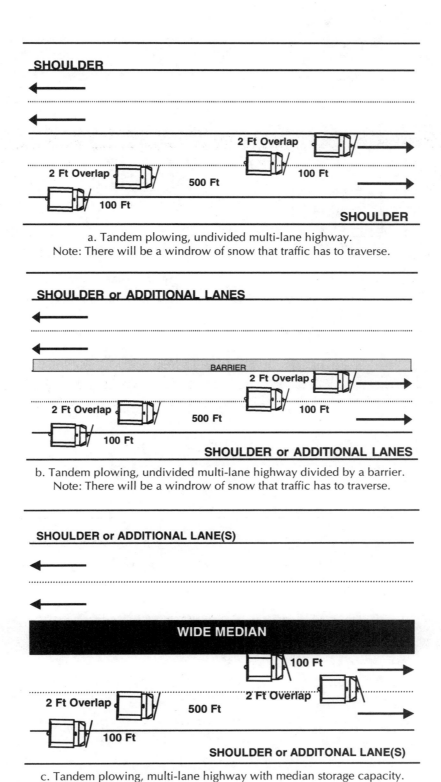

a. Tandem plowing, undivided multi-lane highway.
Note: There will be a windrow of snow that traffic has to traverse.

b. Tandem plowing, undivided multi-lane highway divided by a barrier.
Note: There will be a windrow of snow that traffic has to traverse.

c. Tandem plowing, multi-lane highway with median storage capacity.

Figure 13. Examples of Tandem Plowing Patterns.

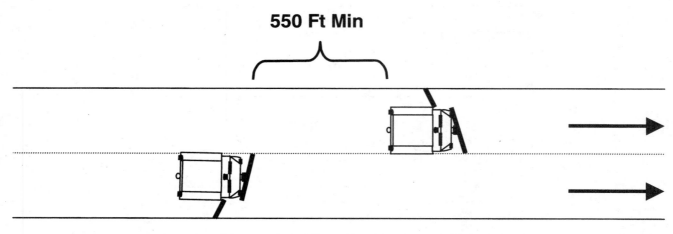

550 Ft Min

a. Two-lane, one-way traffic with center storage using wings.

in one direction on very wide highways, the last truck(s) in line may have to clear smaller areas or have higher

b. Two-lane, two-way traffic, using a wing.

Figure 14. Examples of Two-Lane Plowing Patterns.

horsepower due to the potentially large accumulation of snow on the side from the other trucks.

The availability of a snow storage area, prevailing wind, and the cast capability of the plows determine the ultimate location of deposited snow. If there is sufficient median width, some of the plowed snow can be stored there. If there are prevailing cross winds, most of the snow should be plowed downwind to minimize the "snow fence effect" of windward side snow banks. If the plows can only cast snow in one direction, there will be only one option. Issues related to the placement of snow against median concrete barriers and guardrails are discussed below.

There are other techniques for plowing multi-lane highways that depend on equipment availability and local plowing policy. These techniques provide spacing between plows to allow traffic to pass. However, to the extent possible, traffic should not be allowed to pass through a windrow of plowed snow on the highway.

Ramps and intersections on multilane highways should receive priority treatment since traffic from the mainline has to have a place to go. Many ramps increase in grade as they leave the mainline highway. If plowing is not done in a timely manner, motorists could get stuck on these ramps.

Two-Lane/Two-Way Highways

There are few options for two-lane highways. Starting at the centerline, snow has to be plowed to the right. Intersections should be cleared in the same plowing operation by carrying snow around the corner of intersecting roads and quickly depositing it to the right of the road. If sufficient equipment is available, through plowing of priority routes may be possible with other equipment clearing intersections.

Grid Systems

Typically, priority streets need to be cleared first. In cities and suburbs having grid systems of lower priority roads and streets (all with two-way traffic), plow operators should use a series of continuous right turns while moving through the grid.

Cul-de-Sacs

Cul-de-sacs usually require some special plowing techniques. Some of these techniques include using a one-way plow to plow the main road beyond the cul-de-sac, then carefully backing up and plowing from the left of the centerline of the cul-de-sac toward the island making passes as necessary. The non-island side of the cul-de-sac is plowed in the last pass and the plows can then continue on the main road.   Variations of this procedure that involve "wrong-way" plowing or reversible plows could minimize windrows in driveways.   Some agencies utilize lighter, more maneuverable equipment for this purpose.   Examples of cul-de-sac plowing techniques are shown in figure 15.

Agencies should review their cul-de-sac plowing procedures to be consistent with the type of storms they receive and with melt water runoff.   Plowing to the center of the cul-de-sac causes melting/re-freezing across the cul-de-sac pavement, but is popular with residents because their driveways are not blocked.   Plowing away from the cul-de-sac center has the opposite effect.

Alleys and Dead-ends

The recommended technique for alleys and dead-ends depends on the availability of snow storage area and maneuverability. If there is sufficient area, plow in, turn around and plow out if possible or back out and plow in again as necessary. If there is no snow storage area, the snow has to be removed by loaders and stockpiled for removal or stored elsewhere.

Controlling Melt-water

Frozen melt-water on the highway presents a dangerous condition because it is usually unexpected by the motorist. Plowing snow beyond the shoulder break on the high side of banked curves and pavements having one-way cross slope helps reduce melt-water running across the pavement. Drainage facilities in areas where melt-water may accumulate on the roadway should be kept clear.

Managing Windrows

It is best not to leave windrows of plowed snow on the highway, although equipment availability and highway geometry often necessitate leaving windrows on the highway. Plowing procedures should be designed to leave highway windrows in place for the shortest time possible. Casting the snow further can minimize the size of the windrow. Combinations of faster plowing speeds, the use of "high cast" plows and larger angles of attack can accomplish this.

Off-road windrows or stored snow can cause sight-distance and melt-water problems. Sight distance problems are most serious with

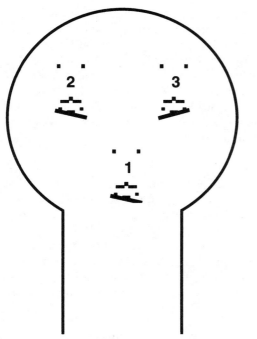

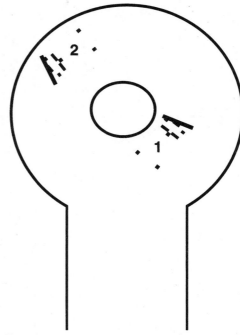

a. Cul de sac with no center island, using a reversible plow. Plow the cul de sac out: The first pass (1) plows the center out; subsequent passes (2) amd (3) plow out their respective sides to the outside of the roadway to the boulevard.

b. Cul de sac with center island, using reversible plow. The first pass, plow toward the center island. Second pass, plow toward the driveways. All snow may be plowed toward the island to eliminate driveway berms.

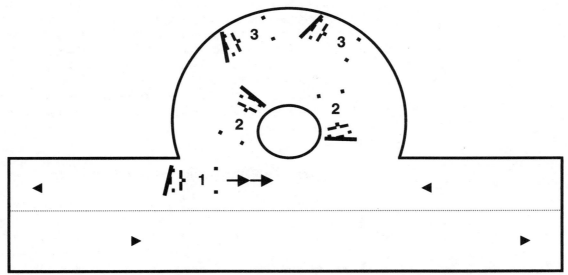

c. One-way plow option: Plow driveway side to slightly past maid road junction (1). Backup to the island. Plow toward island twice until snow runs out (2). Plow the driveway side (3). Continue on the main road.

Figure 15. Cul de Sac Plowing Patterns.

high banks that obscure driveways and intersections. Plowing procedures that move intersection snow at least ten meters beyond the intersection before it is piled up are appropriate. Higher speed plowing will deposit the snow further from the highway and spread it out, but runs the risk of damaging private property. When dealing with individual driveway mouths is practical, pile snow on the down-stream side if possible. Residents and businesses should be urged to clear a snow pocket upstream of their driveway to allow the snow to be cast into the pocket and reduce the windrow across the driveway.

In urban-business areas with wide streets, sufficient median snow storage area, and proper drainage for melt water, it may be possible to plow all highway snow toward the center. This practice, made possible by reversible, left casting, or wrong-way plowing procedures, eliminates some of the sight-distance problems at driveways, and allows parking and access to parking meters without utilizing snow removal operations. Plowing to elevated medians that allow snowmelt to drain back to the pavement should be avoided.

Applying Snow and Ice Control Materials

The application strategy, rate, and distribution pattern for snow and ice control materials may vary each time a materials spreader leaves the stockpile. After the ice control treatment for prevailing conditions has been selected, the final step is to get the designed treatment in the right location at the right time. There are a number of techniques for the application of solid chemicals and pre-wetted solid chemicals that can optimize treatment effectiveness, depending on whether anti-icing or deicing is desired. Experience with applying liquid chemicals has been limited to spreading nearly full pavement width. Other patterns for lower level of service goals may be appropriate. Figures 16 and 17 illustrate examples of spreading patterns.

Two Lane, Two Way Traffic Highways (One lane each way)

The most effective way to treat two-lane, two-way traffic highways is to spread the ice control chemical in the middle third of the highway so that the cross slope of the highway and traffic will distribute the chemical fairly quickly across the entire pavement. When performing simultaneous plowing and spreading operations, care must be taken not to plow chemicals off too quickly. Set the spreader to spread only in the plowed path. If plowing is not anticipated, spread the entire middle third on the "out" run of an "out and return" route. It is acceptable to have a truck on the road not spreading if it is part of a planned strategy.

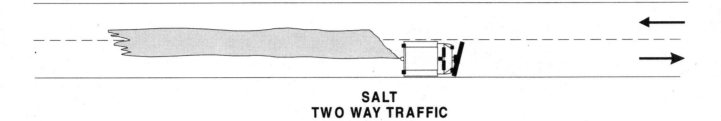

**SALT
TWO WAY TRAFFIC**

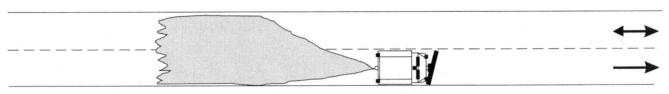

**SALT OR ABRASIVES
ONE OR TWO WAY TRAFFIC**

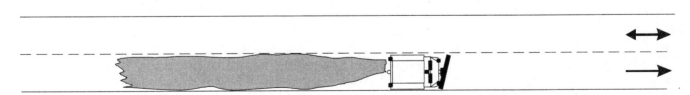

**SALT OR ABRASIVES
ONE OR TWO WAY TRAFFIC**

Figure 16. Examples of spreading (not plowing) patterns for two-lane roads.

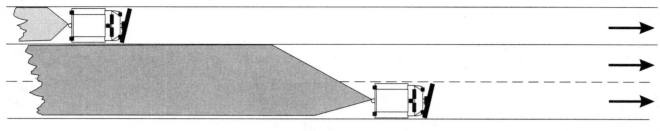

**SALT OR ABRASIVES
ONE WAY TRAFFIC**

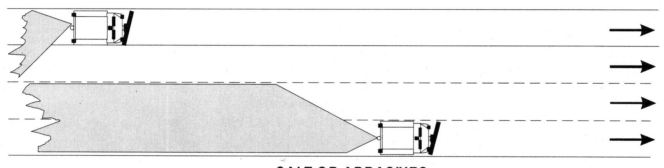

**SALT OR ABRASIVES
ONE WAY TRAFFIC**

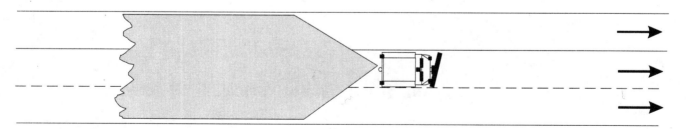

**SALT OR ABRASIVES
ONE WAY TRAFFIC**

Figure 17. Examples of spreading (not plowing) patterns for multi-lane roads.

Multi-Lane Highways

Most agencies spread ice control chemicals on multi-lane highways as near full width as possible. Care must be taken not to spread beyond the pavement limits. Narrow bands of material near the high edge of each lane are also effective.

Parking Areas, Driveways and Walkways

For parking areas, driveways, and walkways, spreading ice control chemicals as evenly as possible over the entire paved area is recommended. These areas are suited for treatment with anti-icing solid chemicals because traffic will not displace the material from the surface.

Hills, Curves, and Intersections

Because of the higher friction requirements on hills, curves, and intersections, many agencies use a higher application rate on these locations than on straight sections of highway. On lower level of service highways, these locations are sometimes the only areas that receive treatment. When doing special treatment at intersections, it is important to carry the treatment beyond the point where traffic normally backs up in snow and ice conditions.

Bridges and Other Elevated Structures Not Resting on Earth

Elevated structures are likely to be colder than the adjacent pavement in the fall and at other times when there is a rapid, severe, decrease in air temperature. It is appropriate to increase the application rate on these structures so that critical dilution will not occur or will occur at about the same time as the surrounding pavement. Toward spring, when air temperatures are warming, structure temperatures are likely to be warmer than the surrounding pavement, and higher application rates are not necessary.

Strong Crosswinds

When spreading in strong crosswinds, the spreader should be kept upwind of the intended spread location. Spreading may not be appropriate if the wind is too strong.

Banked or Elevated Curves

The desired spread pattern should be kept on the high side of elevated curves. As the chemical works, chemical brine will migrate over the remainder of the pavement.

Changes in Maintenance Jurisdiction or Level of Service

Dramatic change in the pavement friction sometimes occurs where maintenance jurisdiction or mandated level of service changes, resulting in a dangerous, unexpected road condition. Appropriate signing or transitioning of the level of service treatment should be used to alert motorists.

The Worst Case Weather Scenarios

The worst case weather scenarios include excessive amounts of water or ice as found in blizzard conditions, including intense snowfall, wind, and very cold temperatures. Snow and ice control chemical treatment can be quickly diluted, rendering it virtually ineffective. If the pavement temperatures going into and coming out of a blizzard are expected to be low, then plowing is probably the best strategy. If, after the blizzard, pavement temperatures are still very cold, using abrasives as necessary will allow chemical de-icing to work until warmer temperatures occur. If the pavement temperatures throughout and after the blizzard are likely to be fairly warm, treatment with an ice control chemical before or early in the storm followed by plowing throughout the storm will make de-icing at the end of the storm much quicker.

Rapidly accumulating freezing rain is another serious snow and ice control problem. The best strategy to deal with freezing rain is to apply solid ice control chemicals at a high rate in very narrow bands in the high side wheel path of each lane. This treatment creates the best opportunity to provide a location in each lane that will produce enough friction to allow vehicles to stop and steer.

In situations where falling and/or blowing snow make visibility near zero, it is a good idea to get snow and ice control vehicles well off the road. Operating snow and ice control vehicles in these conditions is a risk to everyone involved.

Getting the Application Rate Right

Application rates for ice control chemicals are usually specified in pounds per lane mile or kilograms per lane kilometer, although a more meaningful application rate would be to specify the application rate in mass per area, such as grams per square meter. This application rate requires knowing the width of a lane. However, spreaders are usually calibrated to deliver a discharge rate in pounds per mile or kilograms per kilometer. It is important to understand this relationship to ensure that the proper application rate is being used. The application rate is the number of kilograms dispensed per kilometer (the discharge rate) divided by the number of lanes being treated. Table 13 demonstrates that relationship for one, two, and three-lane treatments:

Table 13. Material Discharge and Application Rates.

Discharge Rate (kg/lane-km)	APPLICATION RATE (kg/lane-km) Number of Lanes Being Treated		
	1	2	3
28	28	14	9
56	56	28	19
84	84	47	28
112	112	56	37
140	140	70	47
168	168	84	56
196	196	98	65
224	224	112	75
252	252	126	84
280	280	140	93

Application Techniques for Abrasives

Abrasives are applied to provide temporary friction improvement. They are usually applied nearly the full width of the traveled surface. A higher application rate is often used on locations where the friction demand is higher, such as hills, curves, and intersections. It is not necessary to treat bridges and other cold spots with a higher application rate unless there is a demand for an increased friction. On facilities having a low level of service, areas with a higher friction demand are often the only areas treated.

Abrasives are usually mixed with ice control chemicals prior to application to allow workable stockpiles, flowable material in spreaders, and the ability to stick to the ice in sandpaper fashion. Some agencies have found that spraying the abrasives with a liquid ice control chemical as they leave the truck aids in sticking the abrasives to the ice, while other agencies have found that heated abrasives, without ice control chemicals, also store, flow and stick well.

The prescribed application rate for abrasives varies between agencies. The typical range is from 28 to 340 kilograms per lane kilometer for "natural" abrasive materials and less for "lightweight" manufactured or process byproduct material (bottom ash, slag, cinders, etc.) and some naturally occurring lightweight materials.

Loading, Hauling, and Disposing of Snow

Loading, hauling, and disposing (LHD) of snow is usually a post-storm activity, although there are situations where it may be required during an event. The removal and disposal of snow from alleys, narrow channeled sections, and other areas where there is no snow storage available are typical situations. An event may be so intense that snow storage areas are quickly filled, and LHD is required to reestablish traffic patterns through the area.

Disabled and Abandoned Vehicles

Many agencies have the policy and capability to remove disabled and abandoned vehicles from areas of the roadway that interfere with snow and ice control operations. This practice is most often used on designated priority routes where traffic flow is. During emergency and blizzard conditions, some agencies use large front-end loaders with their buckets filled with snow to push vehicles from critical areas, which causes surprisingly little vehicle damage. Other agencies tow vehicles to specified areas for reclaim. Agencies should review liability potential and provide proper training to those involved in this work.

Plow operators or patrolling supervisors usually identify vehicles that are subject to removal or relocation. Operators should check on the physical well being of the vehicle occupants (if any) prior to removing the vehicle. Occupants should not be in their vehicles during these operations.

Inoperative, Stuck, and Disabled Equipment

Dealing with inoperative, stuck, or disabled equipment during snow and ice control operations is no small task. Stuck equipment can usually be easily extracted. All snow and ice control trucks should carry tow chains of appropriate size and length, and trucks in the vicinity of a stuck vehicle can be diverted to help unless a dedicated vehicle is available for this purpose. Trucks not seriously disabled may be checked and repaired in the field by a mechanic with appropriate tools and parts. If the problem is more complex, the equipment must be taken to a repair facility by tow truck or trailer transporter for repair by agency or contracted personnel.

In winter, snow and ice control equipment that is in for repair or maintenance should be given priority status. If inventory includes usable equipment that is about to be liquidated, it may be put in service until the inoperative equipment comes back on line. Since most agencies do not have spare equipment, the near liquidation equipment represents the next-best alternative. Keeping spare equipment in the range of ten percent of the fleet, using in-house, leased or rented equipment, is desirable assuming that ninety percent of the fleet is operational.

If sufficient equipment is unavailable, contingency plans should be devised for dividing the snow and ice control responsibility among the available equipment or for bringing in additional resources. For example, less desirable loading equipment, such as hydraulic excavators, cranes, tractor-backhoe-loaders, and small loaders, may have used to accomplish loading tasks. Borrowed, leased, or rented equipment should be considered if the need is acute or equipment is likely to be unavailable for a long period of time.

Special Areas to Consider in Storm Management

Several highway, road, and street areas, such as structures, at-grade railroad crossings, and interchanges deserve special consideration during snow and ice control operations.

Structures

Elevated structures tend to freeze before the surrounding pavement and generally track air temperature closer than pavement on grade. If over water, elevated structures could be more prone to black ice and frost. Given the temperature variations, these structures may require more ice control chemical than adjacent pavement in order to achieve the same effectiveness. If non-corrosive materials such as CMA are applied on long structures and chloride-containing products are applied on the adjoining roads, the applications used on the structure should extend at least a mile beyond each end of the structure to minimize chloride material tracking onto the structure.

Plowed snow on bridges requires special attention because it presents a hazard to features or motorists below if snow is plowed off the bridge. Some type of fencing or other containment is usually installed on bridges over vulnerable features. The contained snow on bridges is usually removed with trucks, snow blowers, or loaders after the storm to decrease dead load, control melt water, and provide storage space for the next snow storm. After lighter snowfalls, snow on shorter, narrower bridges can sometimes be removed by bulldozing (plow having close to a 0° attack angle) snow for the length of the bridge and off to the side at the end. This practice may require additional traffic control and protection since it usually requires multiple passes as well as backing into traffic during the operation. Operators should plow slowly to minimize the possibility of snow falling over the edge of the bridge.

At-Grade Railroad Crossings

Plow blades should be raised slightly while crossing tracks to prevent them from hanging-up on the rails. Operators should always stop and look both ways before slowly crossing the tracks. Some agencies require the removal of windrows and snow berms on the tracks as part of the plowing operation.

Interchanges

Timely plowing of ramps at interchanges is necessary to allow movement of exiting and entering traffic. While reversible plows are a great aid in effectively plowing ramps and interchanges, lighter, more maneuverable trucks may also be beneficial in such operations.

Super-Elevated Curves and Steep Grades

Steep grades are a problem because of the tendency of tractor-trailers to get stuck, even in light snow, effectively closing the road. Snow and ice control vehicles often have a difficult time getting to problem areas through backed-up traffic. Many agencies use a short cycle time and very high chemical application rates, often in combination with the routine use of abrasives in these areas.

Deep cuts and Other Shaded Areas

The absence of direct sunshine in pavement increases the potential for icing. As a result, these areas require more ice control chemicals than required for warmer areas to obtain equivalent results.

Narrow Channeled Areas

Some agencies use enough ice control chemicals in narrow channeled areas to melt all snow and ice.

Maintaining Drainage Facilities

Proper highway drainage must be maintained whenever there is a potential for significant snowmelt and/or rain events. Drainage maintenance techniques are discussed below.

Poor or Trapped Drainage Areas

Plowed snow should not be deposited where it could interfere with existing drainage or add to the drainage load as melt water.

Closed Drainage Systems

The openings to closed drainage systems should be cleared prior to anticipated runoff or rain. Because openings are often difficult to locate when under snow windrows or piles, agencies usually mark the locations with paint marks on the pavement and/or tall poles or stakes near the opening. In the event an element of a closed drainage system freezes up, it could be thawed with steam or ice control chemicals.

Open Drainage Systems

Little snow and ice maintenance is required in open drainage systems. In areas receiving significant snowfall and cold temperatures, snow covered culvert ends may actually keep the culverts from freezing. When significant runoff is anticipated, culvert ends should be cleared of snow and ice. Frozen culverts can also be thawed with steam or ice control chemicals.

Ice Jams

Ice jams on rivers and streams can cause damage to bridge elements as well as upstream flooding. Small jams caused by debris located downstream from bridges can be broken up mechanically with a crane and a "headache ball" or clamshell bucket if there is a suitable platform to support the crane and sufficient water flow to remove the dislodged materials. More extensive jams may require explosives if the jams pose a significant threat such as causing flooding or structure damage. Some agencies have stand-by blasting contractors to deal with ice jams. Upstream bridge pier ends situated in jam prone locations may also be protected with special piling and debris catchers/diverters.

Avalanches

Avalanches occur on highways in many locations around the world. Measures to deal with avalanches include structural protection (barriers, energy dissipaters and roofs), scientific methods for determining avalanche potential, road closures when the potential is high, and the controlled induction of avalanches using various explosives or guns. The choice of control measures usually depends on the priority class or the highway(s) impacted.

Other Storm Management Issues

Other storm management issues such as the need to monitor contractor activities and performance and record keeping requirements are discussed in chapter 2.

Special Customer Issues

Snow and ice control agencies must deal with several customer-related issues, such as damage to mailboxes, driveway blockings, and sidewalk plowing.

Damage to Mailboxes

Rural type mailboxes are frequently damaged by snowplowing operations. As mailboxes are usually placed within the highway right-of-way, the governing jurisdiction should have rules and regulations relative to their placement and liability in the event of snowplow damage. The height of the mailbox is defined in the U. S. Postal Regulations, but mounting configurations may be regulated locally. Often, setbacks from the pavement or shoulder and post configurations are regulated features. Some agencies prohibit the use of massive structures that could damage snowplow equipment and act as "roadside hazards" for errant vehicles.

Liability and remedy of mailbox damage varies. Some agencies assume total responsibility for repair or replacement of any mailbox damaged by snowplow activity, while other agencies assume partial responsibility and repair or replace only mailboxes that were directly struck by the plow rather than the snow plume. Some agencies will assume no responsibility at all.

Most agencies make it the owner's responsibility to provide access beyond routine plowing to the mailbox. Some agencies, particularly those requiring larger setbacks, provide mailbox access.

Blocking Driveway Openings

Most agencies make little attempt to limit the amount of snow cast into driveway openings or to remove it. Often, there are prohibitions against placing any snow on the highway, particularly from driveway openings. Special plows with gates are used by some agencies to minimize snow cast into driveways. Higher-speed plowing tends to spread out the snow in driveways and make it more acceptable.

Plowing Sidewalks

Sidewalks are another area of concern to customers. Most municipalities do not provide sidewalk plowing, although some agencies do. Depending on the distance between the highway shoulder and the sidewalk, depositing highway snow on sidewalks can be controlled by limiting plow speed, although it will create higher windrows in driveway openings.

Pedestrian Issues

Certain pedestrian-use areas, such as crosswalks, center islands, bus stops, and handicapped access ramps and cuts may require special attention by snow and ice control agencies if they cannot be cleared and treated as part of the street operations.

Parking

Many municipalities have parking regulations to facilitate snow and ice control and other maintenance operations. One of the most common practices is to allow alternate side street parking every other day or on specified days. An alternate day parking scheme usually allows for complete road clearance within twenty-four hours of the end of the storm. Special snow emergency parking regulations that go into effect by declaration or after a certain amount of snowfall may also be imposed. These regulations are often limited to critical roads and streets that carry large traffic volume or a critical type of traffic. Snow emergency declarations for the purpose of snow removal in commercial and other critical areas are also common. Some municipalities provide parking space in municipal or other lots during snow removal operations.

Having parking regulations is one issue; enforcing them is another. There must be a system in place to timely tow offending vehicles to impound areas or already cleared locations.   Consistent enforcement is an important factor in making parking systems work.

Sensitive Roadside Features

There are some roadside features, such as planters, decorative plantings, architectural effects, landscaping effects, sound walls in restricted roadways, water supplies, and agricultural plantings that may be damaged by snow load or deicing chemicals. Although the first priority of highway agencies is the safety and mobility of the traveling public, the following actions may be taken to provide protection:

* provide temporary structural protection against snow loads;

* cast snow away from sensitive features if possible;

* encourage the municipality and property owners to exclude sensitive structures or vegetation within the zone of snow and ice control influence;

* provide temporary protection for sensitive plantings such as wrappings or screens;

* use environmentally-friendly ice control chemicals such as calcium magnesium acetate or potassium acetate in sensitive areas;

* use abrasives in sensitive areas taking care to avoid the negative impacts associated with abrasives including build-up, moisture retention, clogging drainage systems, and siltation of waterways or guide/guard rails; and

* use the absolute minimum amount of ice control chemical needed for the prevailing condition.

Post-Storm Activities

The after-storm snow and ice control activities are almost as important as the primary operations of plowing snow and spreading ice control chemicals and abrasives.

Melt Water Control

Preventing snow and ice melt water from getting into the traveled areas of the highway is very important. If plowing procedures cannot deposit snow where melt water avoids traveled areas, the snow has to be moved to a location where it can melt into an off-pavement drainage system. This can be accomplished by loading and hauling, snow blowing, or pushing snow back with loaders and plows.

Proper design and maintenance of the highway cross-section will reduce problems associated with melt water. Properly crowned pavements, open drainage capability on both sides of the road, proper maintenance of shoulder and slope drainage capability, proper design and maintenance of closed drainage systems are all important factors that will help reduce melt-water problems.

Restoring the Function of Highway Safety Features and Signs

Safety features like impact attenuators, guardrail, median barrier, breakaway sign supports, and light poles are designed to minimize damage to errant vehicles and occupants. However, these safety features can become hazards when ice and snow build-up adversely impacts their effectiveness. Therefore, provisions should be made to prevent the freezing of liquid-filled impact attenuators. Sand-filled barriers must contain dry sand or a sand-ice control chemical mix. Solid ice or snow must not be allowed to build up on the traffic side of impact attenuators, median barriers, and guardrails to prevent vehicles from ramping over the top of them. Snow and ice accumulation around the hinge points of breakaway features may hamper their function. Signs that become buried or illegible should be given priority attention in cleaning and restoring.

For guardrails and median barriers, close plowing the snow over the top is recommended and solid snow or ice ramps should be removed. If a median barrier separates close opposing traffic, snow will have to be plowed away from the barrier or temporarily stored along the barrier and removed as soon as possible.

Loading, Hauling, and Disposal of Snow

Loading, hauling, and disposing of snow is routinely required in areas with no snow storage area, certain commercial areas, and some drainage sensitive areas. While it is less often required on major roads (because of adverse effects on traffic flow), it is generally required after a blizzard or very high snowfall.

A variety of equipment is used to remove snow. Snow blowers are generally the most effective means to pick up snow to load into trucks or to cast it well away from the road. Loaders can also be used to pick up snow and load or relocate it and can also be used to charge portable snow melters. Graders can be used to remove snow from tight places and put it in a windrow for pick-up by snow blowers, belt loaders or conventional loaders. Graders can also be used to cut down high banks for snow blower removal and make delineators and other objects visible for snowplow operators.

Disposing of snow is becoming a challenging task in some areas due to contaminants in the snow. Hauled snow is often dumped into rivers and other water bodies, or on large open fields. Portable and fixed snow melters are becoming more popular. Many offer some level of treatment for the discharge water. Surface and underground flowing water systems are also used to carry snow away.

Sight Distance Restoration

Snow banks that interfere with reasonable sight distance, typically at curves and intersections, should be pushed back or removed. Priority removal should be assigned to locations with the highest traffic volume. Figure 18 shows suggested sight distance restoration areas.

Shoulder Clearing and Pushing Back

Shoulders should be cleared to their full width to accommodate disabled vehicles and provide temporary snow storage during the next snowfall. Areas beyond the shoulders can also be pushed back to accommodate future snow and minimize drift potential. Wing plows can be used to bench or shelf these areas, particularly if the shoulder or off-shoulder area is unstable.

Clearing of Special Areas

As discussed earlier, clearance of bridge decks and sidewalks are important workflow considerations. Other areas that should be cleared include curb sections and gutters for drainage, raised and flush median areas, rail crossings, walkways, truck escape areas, and fire hydrants. Snow and ice control chemicals can be applied to gravel beds in truck escape ramps to keep the surface from freezing. Local regulations designate the parties responsible for clearing fire hydrants, typically property owners, fire departments, or highway agencies.

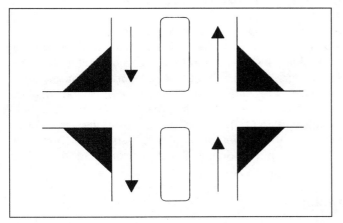

A. Four-lane with two-lane (unsignalized).

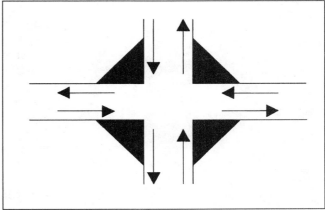

B. Two-lane trunk highway to two-lane trunk (unsignalized).

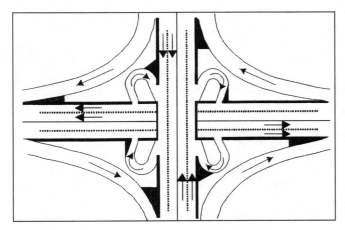

C. Full cloverleaf.

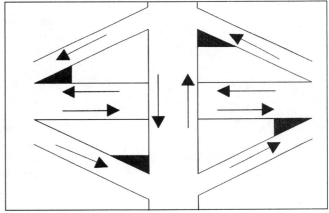

D. Diamond (unsignalized).

Figure 18. Examples of sight-distance clearing. Shaded areas are to be cleared of snow blocking sight distance.

Equipment Repair and Maintenance Activities

After storms and clean-up activities are complete, equipment should be prepared for the next storm. The preparation includes performing a thorough washing and inspection of all lights and safety features, windshields, wipers, plow equipment and mountings, hoses, belts, fluid levels, leaks, tires, tire chains, wheels, suspension systems, brakes, spread control systems, and spreaders. Personnel should ensure cutting edges and shoes have enough material to last through a long storm, and should inventory and restock spare parts and other items (filters, bulbs, and lubricants) that are routinely used.

Asset Inventories

Keeping inventories of people, equipment and materials should be an on-going management function. This task can ideally be performed after storm clean up.

Abrasives Clean-up

If possible, used abrasives should be picked up from the highway environment. Cleanup of abrasives keeps them from getting into the drainage system, reduces air pollution and waterway siltation, and reduces any skidding hazard on the highway. Since sweepers usually contain water in their tanks and are therefore susceptible to freezing, magnesium chloride liquid is sometimes added to the tanks to permit their use in sub-freezing temperatures.

Pavement and Shoulder Repairs

Temporary repairs to pavements and shoulders can ideally be postponed between storms. In moderate climates, these repairs may have more permanence, as hot mix plant or job mix material may be available. Other highway maintenance activities that may be performed between storms include:

* identifying locations which would benefit from snow fence installation

* brush cutting and tree removal;

* guide rail repair;

* sign inventory/replacement;

* stockpile maintenance;

* yard clean-up, recycling and salvage activities;

* equipment maintenance;

* physical features inventory

* equipment calibration;

* training; and

* mailbox repair or replacement.

8 Total Storm Management (TSM)

Introduction

With the large investment in the nation's highway and street systems, motorists expect to travel on well-maintained roadways throughout the year. The great dependence on the highway transportation system for the movement of goods, services, and people has resulted in a demand for more rapid and effective clearance of snow and ice. Environmental concerns center on the uses of snow and ice control chemicals and abrasives in many areas. Therefore, snow and ice control operations must utilize all reasonable means to minimize hazards, slippery road surfaces, costly delays, and abnormal energy consumption by the highway users. These operations must be carried out at the highest level of safety possible for the motoring public and maintenance workers, yet minimize the impact on the environment. These requirements form the basis for the mission of winter maintenance operations that can be stated as follows:

- ❊ provide appropriate levels of service (LOS) to the motoring public;

- ❊ provide highest levels of safety possible for the motoring public and maintenance personnel;

- ❊ perform snow and ice removal in an effective and efficient manner; and

- ❊ preserve the transportation system and roadside environment.

This mission can be accomplished through use of a concept known as Total Storm Management (TSM) which is defined as the process of selecting and applying the appropriate tools and strategies to successfully deal with winter storm conditions. Although TSM was developed for the strategy of anti-icing, the concept can be extended

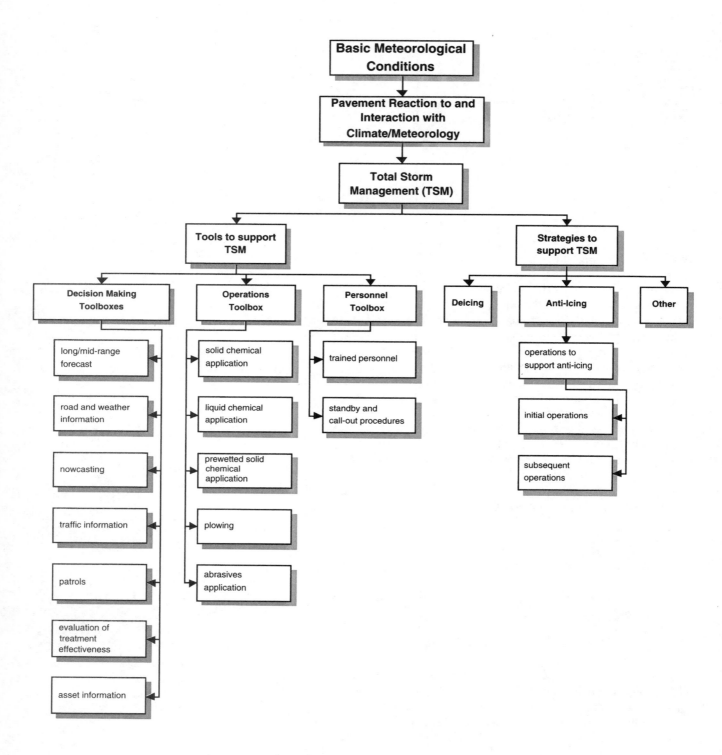

Figure 19. Tools and Strategies for Total Storm Management.

with modification to other strategies. The LOS and the pavement reactions to local meteorological conditions, as shown in figure 19, drive the TSM process for a maintenance area.

The implementation of TSM requires a balance between level of service, storm conditions, and strategies and operations. Management determines the extent to which maintenance services are provided for a specific road section through the assignment of a level of service. For winter maintenance, this requires establishing a prescribed end-of-storm road condition; intermediate conditions that will be acceptable while obtaining this condition; and the frequency and type of snow and ice control operations. Today's challenge for a winter maintenance manager is to provide the appropriate level of service to the public in spite of service-delivery cost increases and decreased maintenance budgets. Consequently, there is a strong need for effective winter maintenance operations throughout the range of storm conditions that can exist in a particular area.

In addition to the level of service, winter maintenance effort will vary with climatic and storm conditions. One significant variable is pavement temperature, which directly influences the formation, development, and disruption of bonds between fallen or compacted precipitation and the road surface as well as the effectiveness of chemical treatments. Pavement temperature is also important when dew point temperatures at or below freezing accompany high humidity levels. Under these conditions, there will be a greater potential for the formation of frost and black ice. Other important climatic factors are the type and rate of precipitation.

Winter maintenance strategies and operations must be tailored to the types of climatic and meteorological conditions that exist in an area. For instance, maintenance forces in mountainous regions must deal with heavy snowfalls (e.g., several feet of snow can accumulate in less than 24 hours) which may occur several times a year. Winter maintenance strategies and operations for these conditions will differ from those for high plains states, where drifting snow may be a major, recurring concern. Conversely, areas such as in the midwest, where winter weather events can include light snowstorms, periods of moderate or heavy snow, freezing rain storms and sleet storms, will require different approaches.

The TSM for such a diversity of winter weather events requires the use of a wide range of tools and strategies for successful operations, as described in the following sections. This information is presented in more detail in a recent FHWA publication dealing with anti-icing operations.

Tools to Support TSM

The tools needed to support TSM include decision-making, operations, and personnel toolboxes. These toolboxes are broken down into tools pertaining to information sources, capabilities, and procedures that are required for a given operation.

Decision-Making Toolbox

The decision-making toolbox includes the following tools:

* ❄ long mid-term weather forecasts;

* ❄ road and road weather information;

* ❄ nowcasting;

* ❄ traffic information;

* ❄ patrols providing information on weather and pavement conditions;

* ❄ asset information; and

* ❄ evaluations of treatment effectiveness.

Each of these seven tools is briefly discussed below. The role the media and other agencies can play in facilitating winter maintenance operations is discussed in chapters 2 and 7.

Long/Mid-Term Weather Forecasts

A rational decision by maintenance managers concerning whether or not to initiate a treatment and what treatment to apply can only be made if good weather information is available for the area under consideration. This information includes forecasts regarding when precipitation is expected to start and what form it will be; air temperatures; temperature trend during and after the storm; dew point temperatures; relative humidity ranges; wind speed and direction; and the sequencing of storms. One source of this information on a regional or national basis is the National Weather Service, but timely forecasts aimed at specific areas and pavement conditions must be obtained through a private forecasting service.

Road and Road Weather Information

Real-time information on pavement temperature, pavement surface conditions, e.g. dry, wet or ice, and some indication of the concentration of a freezing-point depressant (or the freezing-point of a chemical solution) is necessary for making an informed decision on maintenance treatment. Pavement sensors, provided as part of a road weather information system (RWIS), provide the necessary monitoring and warning information. Atmospheric sensors, also part of the RWIS, provide valuable information on the local climatological conditions.

Personnel responsible for resource allocation decisions for snow and ice control operations should have access to the latest weather and road information. This information can help in selecting the level of snow and ice control measures, if any, the appropriate chemical and application rate for the anticipated condition, the scheduling of plowing-only activity, and the re-allocation of maintenance resources, if necessary.

Some states have used thermal mapping information as part of their snow and ice control planning and decision-making process. Thermal mapping, or thermography, is the process of determining thermal profiles of road surfaces using infrared sensors. The temperature data are used to document warm and cold highway spots, help winter maintenance personnel identify critical highway spots, and assist in forecasting pavement temperatures for locations between roadside remote processing unit (RPU) stations. The data can also be used to assist in the siting of RPU stations and to improve the allocation of maintenance resources.

Nowcasting

Nowcasting refers to the use of real-time information for short-term forecasting of the probable weather and pavement conditions or temperatures within one or two hours. Nowcasting relies on the rapid transmittal of data from RWIS installations, radar and satellite images, patrols, and other information sources. Nowcasting is a valuable tool for deciding when to call-in and discharge personnel, and it can be performed by the maintenance manager or be provided by a private weather service.

Traffic Information

Vehicles can affect the wintertime pavement surface in several ways. For example, vehicle tires can compact, abrade, and displace snow or glaze the surface, while the heat from tire friction, engines, and exhaust systems can raise the temperature of the pavement surface. In addition, turbulence resulting from traffic flow can also result in chemicals and abrasives being blown from the pavement while the interaction of vehicle wheel passages and snow and ice control chemicals on the pavement can result in the mixing of chemicals in such a manner to either concentrate or disperse the chemicals. Traffic can also assist in breaking up snow or ice layers whose bond to the pavement have been weakened by chemicals or warm pavement temperature.

Thus, traffic can have both a positive and negative influence on wintertime pavement conditions. Information such as the variation of traffic rate throughout a twenty-four hour period is important for making operational decisions. Plowing and chemical treatments during storms should be made prior to peak traffic intervals.

Patrols

The use of patrols to provide visual observations of weather and pavement conditions, although expensive, can be highly effective as a means for making operational decisions. Trained maintenance personnel are generally better prepared to judge the severity of pavement conditions and to make or recommend appropriate actions. With appropriate training in making assessments of wintertime pavement conditions relative to maintenance actions, state or local highway police can also provide necessary information; without such training, they often overreact to road conditions.

Resource Information

Information on the status of personnel, equipment and materials is an important factor in total storm management. Such information provides the basis for decisions relative to treatment and resource allocation options such as reallocation of personnel and equipment; approval of inter-agency agreements to provide increased capability; and identification of stockpiles of materials that can be accessed through inter-agency agreements or other agency locations.

Evaluations of Treatment Effectiveness

Maintenance decisions relative to which type of action or what type of treatment to make before and during a storm is based upon a variety of information, including historical data. Sources of this information include:

* visual observations of weather and pavement conditions by patrols and operators;

* RWIS data on precipitation, temperature, and pavement conditions;

* indications or measurements of chemical concentrations on the pavement from the RWIS data;

* measurements or indications of friction resistance to sliding;

* weather forecasts;

* weather radar and satellite images; and

* results of treatments for various weather and roadway conditions.

Personnel in each maintenance area benefit from post-storm evaluations of treatment effectiveness as well as the accuracy and usefulness of information that provided the basis for treatment decisions. This evaluation is useful for identifying areas in need of improvement and potential changes in treatment strategies. A post-season review of treatment and information effectiveness is also helpful in identifying changes needed in services, equipment, material, and route configurations. The review can also help identify changes needed in personnel procedures and identify training needs.

Operations Toolbox

* The operations toolbox includes the following tools:

* solid chemical and abrasives application;

* liquid chemical application;

* pre-wetted solid chemical application; and

* plowing.

Solid Chemical and Abrasives Application

The solid chemical application task refers to solid materials, solid material spreaders, and solid chemical storage facilities. The material and equipment requirements for solid chemical applications are similar to those used currently by most winter maintenance agencies. The solid chemical most commonly used for road treatment is salt, or sodium chloride. A mixture of solid sodium chloride and solid calcium chloride has been used by some agencies, and straight calcium chloride has been used in some instances. However, solid CMA is infrequently used because of its cost.

Dry chemicals are applied to the roadway mainly by means of a hopper type spreader or a dump body with an under-tailgate spreader. Figure 20 shows one type of hopper spreader. These devices are capable of spreading free-flowing granular material (including salt, abrasives, and sand/salt mixtures) over a width ranging from three feet (1m) to forty feet (12m). Generally, hopper spreaders are self-contained units that are mounted on dump trucks in the winter, but removed and stored during other seasons so that the trucks can be used for other maintenance work. These units consist of a V-box body, discharge/feed conveyer, spinner disk, power drive, and other necessary components. A full-length feed system such as a full-length belt, chain-drag belt, or a longitudinal auger, is installed at the hopper's base with a speed control provided in the truck cab.

Figure 20. Hopper spreader (the Michigan "wishbone") on truck with under-body plow.

The tailgate spreader is a self-contained unit that replaces the tailgate on a dump body and is easily installed and removed. These devices consist of an external small hopper, an auger feed mechanism, hydraulic driver system, and spinner disc. Truck bodies supporting material distribution spinners behind the cab and providing traction for the drive wheels by distributing material in advance have been used. These truck bodies and those that support tailgate spreaders have to be raised periodically to move materials to the spreader. As a result, care must be taken when used near low wires, trees, and bridges.

Both tailgate and hopper spreaders have been used successfully during deicing and anti-icing operations. Control of material application rates from both types of spreaders can be accomplished manually by operators or automatically relative to the vehicle's speed (ground-speed-oriented controllers).

Zero velocity spreaders are becoming more popular with maintenance forces. These spreaders distribute solid chemicals and solid chemical/abrasive mixtures from the rear of the truck and place the material on the pavement at near-zero velocity relative to the road surface. This feature helps prevent the loss of material from the pavement caused by particle bounce from a spinner-disk distributor or truck speed. Zero velocity spreaders can be made in either a hopper or tailgate configuration. Ground-speed-oriented controllers are available for most types of units.

Regardless of the type of spreader used for snow and ice control operations, it is extremely important to calibrate it to ensure that the desired quantity of material is actually being applied. All equipment should be calibrated before winter operations begin including checking the manufacturer's calibration on new equipment delivered from the factory. Also, it is a good practice to recalibrate the spreader equipment after any maintenance is performed on the spreader/truck system, including the hydraulics. Chapter 7 and appendix B-4 identify procedures for calibration.

Storage requirements and facilities for solid chemicals and solid chemical/abrasive mixtures are discussed in chapter 5.

Liquid Chemical Application

The liquid chemical application task relates to liquid chemical application equipment, chemical solution production facilities, and chemical solution storage facilities. Each of these items is briefly discussed below.

There are basically two types of liquid application equipment for highway use. One type uses spinners consisting of either multiple rotating disks or a single disk. The other type uses nozzles on a distributor bar. Figure 21 shows a spray bar system. Either spreader can be chassis-mounted, a slip-in unit that can be placed temporarily on the bed or frame of a dump truck and removed during the off-season, or it can be a trailer or tow-behind unit.

Until a few years ago, most liquid spreaders were made in Europe and Scandinavia. Several U. S. firms now provide highway spreader equipment and spreader components for distributing liquid chemicals and pre-wetted solid material.

Liquid spreaders are better suited for anti-icing than deicing operations, but there is not enough information in the literature to suggest which type of liquid spreader is the most reliable or effective for anti-icing operations. Some nozzles can have problems with plugging unless the design incorporates large spray nozzle orifices. (0.25 inch (6mm) or larger). Generally, stream nozzle patterns are more effective than fan or cone patterns. If the nozzles are too small, the unit will dispense such a fine mist that it disperses before hitting the pavement surface. Spinner disks can dispense liquid droplets that are too large to provide a uniform coating of the pavement surface. Regardless of the type of liquid spreader, the control of the liquid application rates is best achieved with ground-speed-oriented controllers.

Figure 21. Liquid chemical application using a spray bar (courtesy of Bristol Co.).

Some highway agencies have modified existing spreader equipment before investing in new equipment. Homemade equipment consisting of non-corroding tank, PVC tubing (for piping and drilled for a spray bar) with or without a pump has been successfully used. Asphalt distributor trucks, liquid fertilizer spreaders, and spreaders used to spray for weed control have been modified and successfully used for winter maintenance operations by a few agencies. Sample equipment acquisition and modification specifications are shown in appendices C-3 and C-4.

General experience has shown that liquid chemicals can be successfully applied at speeds up to 25 to 35 mph (40 to 55 km/h) for spinner type spreaders and at speeds to 40 to 50 mph (65 to 80 km/h) for spray-bar type spreaders. Turbulence behind the spreader truck prevents a uniform distribution pattern at higher application speeds.

It is extremely important to calibrate liquid spreaders to ensure that the desired quantity of liquid is being applied. All equipment should be calibrated before winter operations begin, and it is a good practice to perform this calibration periodically during the winter. Nozzles and filters need to be checked frequently for function and output. Changes in settings may be required as a result of wear of mechanical linkages, components, and hydraulic systems.

Several highway agencies have found it is economical to produce their own chemical solutions. This is particularly true for sodium chloride brine and CMA solutions. Descriptions of representative chemical production facilities for salt brine and liquid CMA are given in a recent FHWA publication.

Liquid chemical storage requirements obviously differ from storage requirements for solid material. Aspects of liquid chemical storage requirements are discussed in chapter 5.

Pre-wetted Solid Chemical Application

The task of pre-wetted solid chemical application relates to solid chemical and solid chemical/abrasive mixtures, prewetting techniques and equipment, and chemical solution and solid material storage facilities. Pre-wetting of a solid chemical can improve the effectiveness of the solid in many ways. Advantages of prewetting include:

* liquid added to the solid chemical surface accelerates the solutions generation process;

* a tendency towards less waste of pre-wetted solid chemical because pre-wetted solid adheres to the road surface better;

❅ faster effect of the chemical; and

❅ increased spreading speed in some circumstances.

Sodium chloride, road or rock salt, has been the solid material most commonly used when applying prewetted chemicals in both anti-icing and deicing operations. Salt/abrasive mixtures have also been prewetted.

Pre-wetting solutions can be made from sodium chloride, calcium chloride, magnesium chloride, potassium acetate, or CMA. Water alone has been used as a pre-wetting agent, but only when used at higher temperatures because of the risk for freezing in the truck-mounted storage tank, in the supply line to the nozzles, or at the nozzles themselves. Further discussions of chemical solutions pertinent to the application of pre-wetted solids are contained in the FHWA report .

Pre-wetting can be accomplished by one of three methods. First, a pre-wetting chemical can be injected into the material stockpile at a specified dosage. Second, a liquid chemical can be sprayed onto a loaded spreader or on the material as it is being loaded into the spreader. Third, an on-board spray system mounted on the spreader and/or dump truck can add a liquid chemical at the time of spreading. The pros and cons of these three methods of pre-wetting are also discussed in the FHWA report.

As with all spreaders, periodic calibrations should be made and any deviation in the spreader output should be investigated. Also, when on-board pre-wetting systems are used, periodic inspections of the solid material being dispensed should be investigated to ensure that the desired amount of pre-wetting is being achieved. The actual spreading speed used during operations must be selected to ensure uniform material distribution is being achieved. Finally, ground-speed-oriented controls should be used to achieve as uniform a distribution as possible.

The pre-wetting equipment in use by highway agencies is not totally trouble free. Failures of electric pumps and the clogging of spray nozzles have been reported and well as the discovery that the add-on hydraulic system in some designs was not fully compatible with the truck's hydraulic system. The chemical solution production and storage facilities needed for pre-wetting operations are generally the same as those needed for liquid applications.

Plowing

The role of snowplowing in either deicing or anti-icing operations is to remove as much snow and loose ice as possible before applying chemicals. Plowing is all that will be necessary if the pavement and snow are both cold and dry and the snow is not adhering to the pavement.

There are many types of snowplows. These include one-way front plows, reversible front plows, deformable front moldboard plows, underbody plows, side wing plows, and plows designed specifically for slush removal. Various cutting edges are also available in carbide inserts, steel, synthetic polymers, and rubber. Slush blades have been successfully used in limited areas where wet slush and near-freezing temperatures are common.

Brooming is another technique for removing snow that is loose or not bonded to the pavement surface. Brooming can clear the surface fairly well and significantly reduce the need for ice control chemicals. Brooming will not remove compacted snow and ice and it is most effective on areas that receive little or no traffic between broomings.

Personnel Toolbox

The personnel toolbox contains the following tools:

> ❋ **personnel training for decision making and operations; and**

> ❋ **standby and call-out procedures.**

Personnel Training for Decision Making and Operations

An effective Total Storm Management program requires the training of all personnel, from managers to supervisors to operators, in the details of the program. Anti-icing strategies may involve non-conventional methods and materials and requires more information for effective decision making. Emphasis must therefore be placed on training, which can be accomplished by a consultant or highway agency staff using material similar to those developed under SHRP and FHWA studies.

Deployment of Personnel

Improving personnel mobilization requires improved standby and call-out procedures. For example, modern weather forecasting techniques provide more time in advance of a storm to plan

operations and determine personnel needs. The weather information needed to initiate call-out procedures must be provided in a timely manner to ensure adequate lead-time for mobilization of resources. Lead-time and information requirements will depend on site conditions. By minimizing the mobilization time, total crew time may either reduce total crew time or extend crew availability. Automated telephone calling systems can assist in streamlining the call-out process. Stand-by and call-out procedures should be consistent with Fair Labor Standards Act (FLSA) and collective bargaining agreements.

Strategies to Support TSM

Three snow and ice control strategies are commonly used to support TSM. Anti-icing and deicing, strategies discussed in detail in chapters 6 and 8, make use of chemicals. A third strategy involves temporary friction improvement or the applications of abrasives. This strategy is effective in very cold weather, for lower levels of service, and when chemical supplies are unavailable.

Anti-icing

Anti-icing, a systematic approach to winter maintenance operations, involves several tasks. For anti-icing to be successful, the maintenance manager must ensure that the timing of the operations is consistent with the objective. This action is a subjective decision based on available information and requires that operations be anticipatory or prompt in nature.

Anti-icing provides an efficient means for maintaining roads in the best condition possible during a winter storm. To prevent snow and ice from bonding to the pavement, anti-icing requires about one-fifth the amount of chemicals that is required to destroy the bond in deicing operations. Therefore, anti-icing has the potential of providing snow and ice control with an increased traffic safety at lower cost than deicing.

Deicing

Deicing operations are commonly initiated only after an inch or more of snow has accumulated on the pavement. Operations typically consist of plowing and treating the highway with chemicals, abrasives, or both. This is generally a straightforward procedure, but it often leads to a compacted snow layer that is tightly bonded to the pavement surface and thus pavement deicing becomes necessary. However, timing, application rate, and material type used in deicing operations can be selected based on available information.

Deicing operations are often costly and provide less safety. Occasionally deicing may require large amounts of abrasives and chemicals to temporarily increase traction levels and destroy or weaken the bond of packed snow. Nevertheless, deicing operations will remain an important element for snow and ice control when lower priority service levels preclude preventive operations or anti-icing strategies are not suitable.

General recommendations for successful anti-icing operations during six distinctive winter weather events are given in reference, identifying the appropriate maintenance actions that should be taken during an initial and subsequent anti-icing operation for a given event. Each action is defined for a range of pavement temperatures and forecast temperature trends. These actions include application of chemicals, singularly or in combination with plowing; application of abrasives; plowing only; or doing nothing, depending on the pavement temperature and other conditions.

Most of the maintenance actions involve the application of a chemical in either a dry solid, liquid, or prewetted solid form. The chemical application rates range between 100 to 200 lb/lane-mile (28 to 56 kg/lane-km) for a light snowstorm and 125 to 400 lb/lane-mile (35 to 113 kg/lane-km) for a sleet storm, depending on conditions and whether the treatment is made during an initial or subsequent operation. More information on the types of winter weather events covered and required application rates is given in chapter 5. Recommended chemical application rates for deicing operations under different conditions can be found in the *Handbook of Snow* (Pergamon Press, 1981).

Application rates for chemical/abrasive mixtures used in deicing operations differ from those required for straight chemicals. The salt/sand application rates for a 3:1 mixture ratio might range from 400 lb/lane-mile (113 kg/lane-km) for light snow at near freezing conditions to over 1,000 lb/lane-mile (280 kg/lane-km) for a heavy snow or sleet storm in the 15-20°F (-9 to -7°C) range. The application rate for a 5:1 mixture ratio of sand and salt may be 1,200 lb/lane-mile (310 kg/lane-km) or less at temperatures down to 15°F (-9°C) but not below this temperature because the application of any chemical in this temperature range may create a problem by causing a wet pavement surface to which dry snow can adhere and begin to build up.

Experience from controlled tests supports the use of less chemicals and abrasives for anti-icing operations than for deicing operations. The level of reduction in chemical and abrasive use depends on how similar the anti-icing operations are to conventional deicing operations.

References

1. Ketcham, S., L. David Minsk, R. Blackburn, and E. Fleege, "Manual of Practice for an Effective Anti-icing Program: A Guide for Highway Winter Maintenance Personnel," Report No. FHWA-RD-95-202, Federal Highway Administration, Washington, D.C., June 1996.

2. Blackburn, R., E. McGrane, C. Chappelow, D. Harwood, and E. Fleege, "Development of Anti-icing Technology", Report SHRP-H-385, National Research Council, Washington D.C., 1994.

3. Ketcham, S., L. David Minsk, and L. Danyuk, "Test and Evaluation Project 28, 'Anti-icing Technology,' Field Evaluation Report," U.S. Army Cold Regions Research and Engineering Laboratory, Hanover, New Hampshire, 1996.

4. `SHRP Snow and Ice Control Showcasing and Implementation, FHWA Contract No. DTFH61-94-C-00177, Federal Highway Administration, Washington, D.C.

5. "Handbook of Snow: Principles, Processes, Management, and Use," Edited by D.M. Gray and D.H. Hale, Pergamon Press, 1981, p 606.

9 Safety and Liability

Safety for Road Users and Crews

Winter weather and road conditions can burden even the most experienced drivers. Snow and ice, poor visibility, and wind make driving treacherous. Winter driving requires safe practices combined with well-maintained and safe equipment. Maintenance personnel have a responsibility to operate safely with safe equipment.

The goal of highway snow and ice control is to provide a safe pavement surface for drivers. Winter maintenance personnel have to use safe practices and procedures in order to attain the level of service established by the agency and expected by the public. Unsafe practices can lead to accidents and lead to equipment or operators being unavailable to do the necessary work. As a result, the public is exposed to increased accident potential.

Safety Programs

The best method of ensuring safe practices among agency personnel is through the introduction of a formal safety program supported by managers at all levels. Maintenance supervisors, lead personnel, and equipment operators should follow and promote safe practices and identify problems that need corrective actions. A good safety program provides many benefits, including:

* reduced operating costs;

* increased productivity;

* reduced cost of equipment repair and loss of use;

* reduced worker lost time;

* decreased rework of efforts;

* safer work environment;

* improved quality of service;

* improved customer (community) relations;

* improved employee stability;

* better worker motivation; and

* improved employee loyalty.

A good safety program requires informed and motivated workers. The following actions have been modified from a Fleet Safety program established by Ohio Casualty Group:

* *Implement steps to develop a safety culture.* Supervisors should be held accountable for safety, just as they are held accountable for productivity, work quality, and efficiency.

* *Identify and correct unsafe behaviors.* Horseplay and improper use of equipment should not be tolerated.

* *Investigate all accidents and near misses to prevent reoccurrence.* Disciplinary action should be considered in repeat offenses.

* *Develop and use a good accident/near miss investigation report* to zero in on accident causes, trends, and corrective actions taken.

* *Communicate results of investigations to employees* as soon as possible to reduce the potential of a recurring loss.

* *Disseminate and distribute appropriate information,* including agency-produced or commercial safety information and industry/trade publications.

* *Develop guidelines for the various snow and ice control procedures,* including safety guidelines for mounting plowing and spreading equipment; mounting tire chains; plowing procedures; using wing plows; storing and handling materials; personal protection gear; accessing/egressing equipment; safe operating condition of equipment; communicating in emergency situations; potential medical emergencies and treatments; fatigue and length of duty issues; backing and turnarounds; safety chains, chocking and blocking; and warning lights on snow and ice control vehicles.

✳ *Keep records of activities* to document the effects of both safe and unsafe practices.

✳ *Encourage friendly competition among personnel* for best safety performance and rewarding winners.

✳ *Include safety awareness in all maintenance training programs.* Rodeos or other hands-on training at snow and ice control workshops or conferences should be organized to foster awareness and to gather information for further dissemination.

✳ *Include safety as a part of quality improvement initiatives.*

Equipment Safety

Providing comprehensive vehicle maintenance is one of the most important considerations for a safety program since poorly maintained vehicles are often unsafe vehicles. Performing regular maintenance functions reduces the possibility of accidents due to vehicle defects and provides numerous benefits, including fewer vehicle breakdowns; lower replacement part costs; decreased overall operating cost; increased service life of vehicles; increased vehicle resale value; enhanced public image; and higher driver morale.

Vehicles requiring maintenance should be repaired as soon as possible. Maintenance personnel should use a triage system to determine the severity of defects and then prioritize the work to correct the most serious maintenance and safety problems first.

Operator Safety

Operators should regularly use checklists to inspect vehicles and other equipment, and note defects and maintenance problems requiring immediate correction. A sample checklist form is shown in appendix B-5. Operators should always carry a minimum complement of safety gear in their equipment. A typical set of gear would include:

✳ accident report forms;

✳ minimum set of tools for minor maintenance;

✳ tire chains;

✳ fire extinguishers;

✳ reflective triangles, breakdown warning signs, or flares;

❄ foul weather gear, including gloves;

❄ hard hats;

❄ flashlight;

❄ first aid kit;

❄ reflective vests; and

❄ traffic control flags.

Safety items should be stowed properly in clearly marked exterior compartments or secured in the vehicle cab, as appropriate. Safety guidelines should emphasize safe equipment operations, including:

❄ seat belt usage;

❄ defensive driving;

❄ safety regulations;

❄ material loading and material (chemical) handling; study material safety data sheets for all chemicals used;

❄ vehicle speed when plowing and applying materials;

❄ vehicle visibility — keeping windows clear of frost and ice, ensuring conspicuity markings, and safety warning lights are in working order;

❄ roadside visibility — prior to winter, ensure proper roadside markers, such as delineator posts, markings and guardrails and other features are in place.

❄ hazard identification — operators must make route runs before winter arrives to identify and note potential hazards; and

❄ human factors — operators must understand sources of stress and physical fatigue in order to address the role of human factors in improving safety and reducing accidents.

Public Safety

Public safety should be the primary consideration of all agency personnel, including snow and ice control personnel. The following guidelines, developed by the Minnesota Department of Transportation provide safety guidelines for the traveling public:

* obey traffic laws;

* avoid making sudden moves;

* avoid pushing snow over bridge rails;

* avoid pushing snow onto sidewalks and into storefronts;

* keep to the right side of the road when oncoming traffic approaches;

* be careful to make sure that the spinner does not throw material at vehicles and pedestrians; and

* report stranded motorists whenever possible.

Guidelines should also address the importance of speed control; vehicle stopping distance and turning radius requirements; skid control corrections; and vehicle preparation and equipping for winter driving.

The traveling public should be included in safety programs. In addition, the media can be used to develop safety awareness in and around snow and ice control equipment and to encourage safe driving practices. A systematic road condition reporting procedure should be prepared by the winter maintenance or law enforcement agency for use in public advisories.

Agency guidelines should also contain procedures for temporary closures of roads in special locations such as mountain passes and sparsely populated areas. Procedures for coordination with media and emergency management services, including police agencies, should be clearly defined and followed to provide the safest environment for agency personnel and the traveling public. Guidelines should discuss procedures for dealing with whiteout situations and ice-covered pavements. Some agencies require that operations cease and equipment be removed from roadways to avoid collisions with motorists and fixed roadway features. Road closure procedures should be implemented, if possible, to ensure motorist's safety.

Liability and Risk Management

Snow and ice control is intended to provide specific levels of service to the roads and their users. The level of service needs to be clearly defined in agency documents and guidelines and be communicated effectively to the public. Guidelines should also emphasize motorists' responsibility to drive appropriately for road conditions. Maintenance personnel should review legal issues that apply to their snow and ice control activities.

Failure to take appropriate action and perform required maintenance when apprised of a certain condition could raise a liability issue. Under the current system of tort liability, legal actions are taken even when agencies perform their functions in a responsible manner. It is therefore necessary for all agency personnel to understand their responsibility and reduce potential for liability concerns.

Agency training programs should address tort liability, including importance of good record keeping of activities performed and conditions that existed; need to continually review agency policies, practices and responsibilities (for example, it is incumbent on the agency to exhaust all reasonable possibilities to correct deficiencies); techniques to manage and limit liability; accident investigation and analysis, including all personnel records and specific observations at all accident scenes; indemnification; and insurance.

Resource Materials

The Local Technical Assistance Program (LTAP) is a good source of information on safety, risk management, and tort liability. Available videos and training materials can be used in periodic training programs. Locations of LTAP Centers can be obtained from state departments of transportation and state divisions of the Federal Highway Administration, or the Colorado Transportation Information Program of the Colorado State University from the Internet at . A listing of materials available from LTAP can be found at . Examples of materials available from LTAP centers are provided in appendix B-6. Additional materials related to liability and snow and ice control can be found in references 3 and 4.

References

1. "Instituting a safety program can reduce your costs," The Ohio Casualty Group of Insurance Companies, 1997

2. *Ice and Snow Removal Manual*, Minnesota Department of Transportation, February 1991.

3. Supplement to Liability of State and Local Governments for Snow and Ice Control, NCHRP Legal Research Digest Number 9, Transportation Research Board, Washington, DC. 1990.

4. The Public Duty Defense to Tort Liability, NCHRP Legal Research Digest Number 17, Transportation Research Board, Washington, DC. 1990.

Special Considerations

Design for Snow and Ice Control

Some features of transportation facilities may adversely impact snow and ice control operations and influence costs, liabilities, and benefits. Therefore, maintenance personnel familiar with snow and ice operations should be part of the highway design process. Features to consider include:

❅ *Drainage Systems.* Open or above ground drainage systems are preferred over closed or below ground systems that require more clearing of snow and ice (grates and inlets), and sometimes freeze, requiring thawing with chemicals or by heating.

❅ *Snow Storage Area.* The design of highway facilities should allow for a sufficient snow storage area since purchasing right-of-way for snow storage at a later date may not be cost effective. In urban areas, availability of sufficient snow storage area may eliminate or reduce the need for snow disposal. In rural locations, availability of a sufficient area to cast or spread out plowed snow will minimize drifting that is sometimes caused by high snow banks near the highway. Full-width shoulders can provide a temporary storage location for plowed snow, a safe stopping area for disabled vehicles, and a recovery zone for out-of-control vehicles.

❅ *Features to Facilitate Winter Maintenance.* The design of highway facilities should consider snowplow routes. The design should provide for crossovers and turnarounds at appropriate locations to accommodate maintenance and emergency vehicles. Deceleration lanes at crossovers and sufficient crossover width should be provided to allow safe operation of snow and ice control trucks. Some agencies feel it is safer not to use crossovers while snow or ice is falling, so they design plow routes to turn around at cross streets or interchanges.

Safety Appurtenances. Highway apertures such as concrete barrier, box beam guardrails and "W" section guardrails tend to collect plowed snow and make certain areas prone to drifting. Therefore the use of cable guardrails, box beams, and other open rail designs should be considered in drift-prone areas.

Channelization Devices. Raised medians and islands are used to control traffic movement, but they also pose some difficult snow and ice removal situations. Use of flush medians and islands should be considered where appropriate.

Pavement Delineation Devices. Raised reflective pavement markers are used in many locations. Installing low profile or recessed pavement markers should be considered in high snowfall areas where plowing operations use metal blades.

Plan and Profile (As Related to Drifting). The economics of earthwork for new and reconstructed highways usually results in a series of cuts and fills. To the extent possible, cut sections perpendicular to prevailing winds and having long fetches (distance to the nearest upwind snow break) should be avoided. Side slopes should be designed to minimize snow being captured upwind of the highway.

Remedial Measures to Solve Operational Problems Associated with Snow and Ice Control

Sometimes little can be done to improve existing conditions. However, the following actions can be taken to improve the efficiency of snow and ice control:

*identify problems using inputs from equipment operators and supervisors;

*develop a systematic plan to correct the deficiencies;

*identify in-house maintenance efforts that can correct deficiencies;

*identify deficiencies that require construction;

*prioritize the list of deficiencies;

*work with design and construction personnel to determine costs and seek funding for the projects; and

*correct the deficiencies as funds and time permits.

Prevention and Protection Systems for Specific Hazards

There are a number of specific hazard situations that do not necessarily occur during snow or ice events. These require special planning and control techniques.

Avalanches and Snow slides

Although avalanches and snow slides are primarily associated with high snowfall and steep mountain slopes, they can cause problems elsewhere. Probable locations are identified over time based on historical occurrence and analysis of favorable conditions.

Active control measures

Active control of avalanches usually consists of road closure, avalanche induction, inspection, and clean up. Before clean-up operations commence, instrumentation and spotters are used to make sure that any potential hazard of reoccurrence is reduced and to warn crews if another avalanche starts. Avalanches are usually induced by explosives that include military artillery projectiles and conventional explosives delivered by a variety of techniques. Site-specific weather forecasting and assessment of ground snow conditions near the inception zone can assist in providing advanced knowledge of the conditions and the need for an active control. Clean up is then accomplished using conventional methods as described in chapter 7.

Passive Control Measures

There are a number of passive measures for controlling avalanche areas. One of the common techniques is to close the area when the avalanche potential is high. Covering of avalanche-prone areas with structural sheds and tunnels is a costly, but effective method of protecting locations in populated areas. Structural diverters and energy dissipaters are installed in areas with a high frequency of avalanches. These devices must be tall enough to protrude above the general snow depth to perform their function. Building reinforcing units to contain the snow may stabilize the inception zone of avalanches. Techniques for sensing the inception of avalanches with load cells and other devices have been routinely used. Automatic road closure devices and companion safety systems based on inception indications are being considered and an experimental wind direction alteration project is currently underway at one location in Wyoming (conversation with Professor Rand Decker, University of Utah).

The Wyoming project involves the installation of snow sails, called *Kolktafeln* in Europe, that disrupt the snow depositional environment in order to prevent the snow layering that precedes avalanches. The snow sails in Europe tend to be permanent wooden structures, ten to thirteen feet tall (3-4m), six to ten feet wide (2-3m), with a three foot (1m) or more gap under the bottom. The project in Wyoming is looking at the use of Kevlar material for seasonal rather than permanent installations. More detail on the snow sail concept can be found in reference.

Blowing and Drifting Snow Control

Controlling blowing and drifting snow on highways has frequently been accomplished by using empirical methods and experience. Work sponsored by the Strategic Highway Research Program (SHRP) resulted in a designed approach to blowing snow control. These passive control methods can be very cost effective, as much as 100 times less costly than mechanical snow removal. The Snow Fence Guide published by SHRP is an excellent source of information.

Highway design features such as cuts and upwind slope design that impact blowing and drifting snow are discussed earlier in this chapter. There are a variety of snow fence configurations that perform well. Design considerations for effective snow fence design in avalanche areas include:

* location of drift or reduced visibility prone areas;

* prevailing wind direction(s) and velocity;

* fetch (upstream of the snow fence) conditions;

* snow load;

* terrain characteristics;

* fence height and length;

* fence porosity (percent of open space);

* fence locations and orientation;

* fence bottom gap (space between the ground and the lowest horizontal portion of the fence; and

* fence set back (distance from feature being protected).

For conventional snow fences to be effective, they must be located at a considerable distance from the area of protection. A blower fence was developed in Japan that is highly effective and can be placed very close to the area being protected. Living snow fences or plantings can be designed in much the same way as conventional snow fences. Because these fences require some time to become totally effective, temporary fencing may be used as an interim measure.

Most agencies do not have the resources to implement blowing and drifting snow control measures at all drifting locations on entire plow routes all at once. Therefore an installation plan that demonstrates the effectiveness of the control measures and spreads the costs over time is recommended. Although initial savings in operational cost may not be realized, there will be immediate safety benefits at these locations where blowing and drifting is controlled.

Warning Systems for Low Visibility

Visibility can be reduced due to snowfall, blowing snow, rain, or fog. Techniques exist for measuring or estimating visibility. For example, many RWIS road sensor sites include devices for measuring visibility and for providing near real-time data that can be used to activate variable message signs or alert officials of the need for road closure or other travel restrictions.

In locations where roadways are monitored by video cameras, traffic operations center video systems can also monitor visibility problems. In addition, advances in RWIS hardware and software allow the use of video cameras at some RWIS locations. Plow operators and public safety professionals conducting routine business can communicate low visibility situations to traffic control or regulatory authorities to take precautionary actions such as speed reduction, warning sign activation, or traffic closures.

Other Potentially Hazardous Situations

The surfaces of certain highway system locations, particularly bridge decks, cold spots, shaded areas, low spots, and moist areas, become slippery earlier than surrounding areas. If the potential for such danger is high, one of the most cost-effective treatments is to apply liquid snow and ice control chemicals to these locations in advance of the anticipated problem. The treatment will remain effective for several days depending on the rate of dilution and event temperature characteristics.

Remote sensors that monitor temperature, moisture, and ice formation may be installed at potentially hazardous sites to aid in predicting and responding to slippery conditions. There are in situ systems that will apply solid snow and ice control chemicals or abrasives by personnel activation from remote locations or by automatic activation in response to sensor data. The dispensers are spaced along the side of the road or bridge deck and apply liquid snow and ice control chemicals. Spray nozzles are placed at various locations within the pavement or bridge deck, on bridge or guardrail, and in curb sections. When using these systems, care must be taken to make sure that the distribution system is working properly and there is sufficient material in the reservoir or hopper at the required times.

Heated pavements and bridge decks have been used with limited success because of the high energy cost (unless there is a local source of waste or natural energy) and recurring plumbing and/or electrical problems. Passive devices such as earth-source heat pipes have been used successfully with no continuing energy added. Heat pumps that use earth heat, geothermal sources, or fossil fuel may become economic to use in special situations. Tests have been conducted at O'Hare International Airport on the use of electrically conductive asphalt to which electric current can be applied, although the electricity cost may preclude its widespread use.

In some areas, agencies have experiment with the use of insulated pavements and bridge decks. However, in the fall, insulated pavement experiences freezing surface temperatures more quickly than surrounding uninsulated sections and ice tends to form on insulated bridge decks but not on surrounding roadways (preferential icing). Pavements enhanced with embedded deicing or ice retardant chemicals have also been tried by some agencies, but results were mixed.

Other Motorist Warning and Driving Aid Features

Pavement sensors associated with RWIS may be used to alert motorists of site specific freezing temperatures and ice formation by automatic or personnel-activated variable or fixed message signs. These data maybe shared with the media and other interested parties by direct linkage or edited re-transmission.

Communication between road patrols and dispatchers/operations centers provides information needed to activate appropriate signage and other notifications. Recruitment of law enforcement personnel for surveillance and the monitoring of over-the-road trucker broadcasts on CB radios are also valuable road condition sources.

Snow markers are an effective means for identifying roadside obstacles and providing a general sense of where the road shoulder is located, especially during plowing operations and limited visibility situations. Therefore, markers should have reflective and highly visible markings, be tall enough to be visible above higher-than-normal snow depths, and be securely implanted or affixed. Markers can be made of almost any material ranging from small trees/brush/branches to metal.

Signage can be obscured when wet plowed or blowing snow adheres to the surface. Treatment with water-repellent coatings can reduce the rate of adhesion. In problematic areas, signs may have to be "tipped" upstream and still remain visible. Sign visibility can be kept by heating or automatic and manual chemical deicing, although they are seldom used for fixed messages and non-internally illuminated signs. Sign relocation to a different wind environment may be possible if it satisfies the requirements of the Manual of Uniform Traffic Control Devices.

Environmental Considerations

All personnel involved in snow and ice control operations should knowledgeable with applicable local environmental laws, rules, regulations, and policy, including storage requirements, acceptable materials, application rates, chemical free or restricted zones, abrasives clean-up requirements, equipment washing requirements, and snow disposal requirements. Close cooperation, coordination, and interaction with environmental regulating agencies is encouraged, as it provides a good understanding of related issues. See chapters 1, 2, 4, 5, and 7 for further discussion of environmental considerations.

Groundwater Contamination

Contamination of ground water is the largest environmental problem associated with snow and ice control operations. Contamination may occur because of improper storage of chemical stockpiles and stockpiles of chemical-abrasives mixtures.   The problem can be corrected by:

* ❄protecting the stockpiles from precipitation with impermeable structural or temporary coverings; and

* ❄placing stockpiles on an impermeable base that is not subject to flooding or run-off.

Unfortunately, financial resources may not be readily available to solve the problem. Some states have grants and low interest loans to help agencies deal with this specific problem.

Vegetation

Certain vegetation species are sensitive to some deicing chemicals. If the vegetation resource is considered valuable, protective measures should be taken. Examples of such measures include:

⁂ changing to non-threatening ice control chemical or abrasives;

⁂ reducing the chemical application rate;

⁂ screening or wrapping the vegetation; and

⁂ replacing vegetation with a tolerant species if the chemical cannot be changed.

Facilities and Equipment

Facilities and equipment exposed to corrosive ice control chemicals should be thoroughly washed after each exposure. Bridges and other highway appurtenances should be washed at the end of the season and protective coatings such as paint should be applied to all corrosion-sensitive surfaces. Sealant and other protection should be applied to electrical connections. Where possible, equipment should be stored under cover or in a weatherproof structural facility.

Air Quality Issues

Fine particulate matter in the air is an increasing environmental concern. Some of the load in the air results from the application and subsequent degradation and dispersion of abrasives. Additional loading can be caused by traction enhancing devices in tires such as studs that degrade and disperse highway pavements. Actions for reducing the air quality problems include:

⁂ limiting the use of abrasives;

⁂ using higher quality abrasives that don't degrade as quickly;

⁂ increasing the use of deicing chemicals;

⁂ removing abrasives as soon after use as possible with sweepers; and

⁂ limiting the use of studded tires.

In general, vehicle emissions are increased when traffic is moving slowly or idling. Providing snow and ice control measures that allow traffic to move is the best control measure.

Surface Water Issues

Surface waters can be adversely affected by loading of snow and ice control chemicals and abrasives. Chemicals can impact some living organisms within flowing and static water bodies although limited impacts have been identified to date. Elevated levels of sodium and chlorides are of concern in surface waters used as public water supplies.

Abrasives in streams and rivers can affect water clarity, change the essential character of stream and river beds, and can have a significant impact on aquatic life by changing bottom and depth characteristics.

Reduction in chemical loading can be achieved by changing chemicals or reducing chemical use. Abrasives loading can be lowered by reduction in use or installing containment facilities that are periodically cleaned.

Habitat Quality

Land habitat issues center primarily on the physical alteration caused the build-up of abrasives and loss of vegetative support provided by some chemical sensitive species. The same mitigation strategies cited above may be used in this situation.

References

1. *Snow Fence Guide*, **Federal Highway Administration Publication No. FHWA-SA-94-087.**

2. Mellor, Malcom. "Wind Baffles for Modification of Snow Deposit", Cold Regions Science and Engineering Monograms, Part 3 - Engineers, Section A3 - Snow Technology, US Army Cold Regions Research and Engineering Laboratory (USACRREL), 1968.

Appendix A: Bibliography

The following represents a sample of publications agencies should consider acquiring for reference. Some agency document titles are generic because the documents might be acquired from more than one agency.

Highway Deicing, Comparing Salt and Calcium Magnesium Acetate, Transportation Research Board Special Report 235, Washington, DC, 1991

D. M. Murray and U. F. W. Ernst. An Economic Analysis of the Environmental Impact of Highway Deicing. Abt Associates, Inc. Report No. EPA 600/2-76-105, May, 1976

D. E. Kuemmel. Managing Roadway Snow and Ice Control Operations. NCHRP Synthesis of Highway Practice 207, Transportation Research Board, Washington, DC, 1994

Byrd, L. Gary. Winter Maintenance Program: Plans for Snow and Ice Control Guide and Snow and Ice Pooled Fund Cooperative Program, NCHRP 20-7 (Task 71) Final Report, Transportation Research Board, Washington, DC, June 1996

Snow and Ice Control Materials Storage and Handling, FHWA-RD-75-524

NCHRP 127, Snow and Ice Control Techniques at Interchanges

Mn/DOT Ice and Snow Removal, 1991

Safety Restoration During Snow Removal - Guidance, FHWA-TS-90-036

Weather Forecasting - Long and Short Range Forecasting for Day to Day Dispatching, Weather Services Corporation, 1991

Curtailing Usage of De-Icing Agents in Winter Maintenance, OECD, Paris, 1989

Optimizing Maintenance Activities, Snow and Ice Control Operations, FHWA TS-77-208

Efficient Personnel Management for Winter Highway Maintenance, Wright, Egly, Berg. Indiana Department of Transportation, 1986

Cost Effective Staffing of Crews During Winter, Rissel, Better Roads, 1985

TRR 506, Better Maintenance: Measuring Quality, Training Personnel, Snow Fences and Deicing Chemicals, 1974

HRR 227, Snow and Ice Control, four reports, 1968

Hegnon and Meyer, Effectiveness of Antiskid Materials, 1968

Environmental Impact of Highway Deicing, EPA 11040 GKK, June 1971

TRR 1157, Deicing Chemicals and Snow Control, 1988

NCHRP Synthesis 24, Minimizing Deicing Chemical Use, 1974

Economic Impact of Highway Snow and Ice Control, FHWA-RD-77-95

Manual for Deicing Chemicals: Storage and Handling, EPA-670/2-74-033

Snow and Ice Control, A Best Practices Review, Office of State Auditor, Minnesota, May, 1995

Statewide Maintenance Operations Research Report, Mn/DOT Office of Maintenance Operations Research, 1995

Use of Salt for Snow and Ice Control, Ontario Ministry of Transport, M-703

The Snow Fighters Handbook, Salt Institute.

State departments of transportation, Guidelines for Snow and Ice Control

State departments of transportation, Operators Manual

State departments of transportation, Training Manual

New York State Department of Transportation, Municipal Contract Manual

4th International Symposium, Snow Removal and Ice Control Technology, Reno, NV, Aug 1996. Preprints Volumes I and II

8th International Road Weather Conference, Birmingham, England, Apr 1996. Proceedings

Manual of Practice for and Effective Anti-icing Program: A Guide for Highway Winter Maintenance Personnel, Publication No. FHWA-RD-95-202, U. S. Department of Transportation, June 1996.

Kuemmel, David A. Development of a Chemical Demand Index for the Minnesota DOT - A pilot Project. Marquette University Center for Highway and Traffic Engineering, Milwaukee, Wisconsin, January 1995.

Öberg, Gudrun. Low Cost Winter Maintenance - Swedish Experiences, VTI särtryck Nr 237, 1995

Kuemmel, David A. Benefit/Cost Comparison of Salt Only vs. Salt/Abrasive Mixtures Used in Winter Maintenance in the USA, Marquette University Center for Highway and Traffic Engineering, Milwaukee, Wisconsin, June, 1996

Ice Detection and Highway Weather Information systems Summary Report , Test and Evaluation Project 011, Publication No. FHWA-SA-93-053, U. S. Department of Transportation, June, 1993

Snow Removal and Ice Control Technology, Transportation Research Record No. 1387, Transportation Research Board, Washington, DC, 1993.

Thornes, John E., R.D. Osborne, J.G. Sugrue. Thermal Mapping and the Prediction of Minimum Road Surface Temperatures, TRRL Research Report 842/362, University of Birmingham, UK, 1985

Road Weather Information System Task Force Report to New Technology Research Committee, Minnesota Department of Transportation, June, 1993

An Evaluation of Weather Information Technologies for Snow and Ice Control Operations, WA-RD 323.1, Washington State Department of Transportation, April, 1993

Perry, A.H., and L.J. Symons (Eds.). Highway Meteorology, E & FN Spon, London, 1991

Road Weather Information Systems Volume 1: Research Report, SHRP-H-350, National Research Council, Washington, DC, 1993

Road Weather Information Systems Volume 2: Implementation Guide, SHRP-H-351, National Research Council, Washington, DC, 1993

NCHRP Research Digest No 204 "Winter Maintenance Technology and Practices - Learning from Abroad" Jan. 1995

Decker, R, Report of Findings of 1994 FHWA/TRB/NCHRP International Winter Maintenance Technology Scanning Tour, Transportation Research Board, August, 1994

Winter Road Maintenance Methods in Finland, Finnish National Road Administration, Helsinki, 1993

Alppivaori, K, A. Leppanen, M. Anila, and K. Makela. Road Traffic in Winter, Finnish National Road Administration, Helsinki, 1995

Savenhed, H. Relationship between Winter Road Maintenance and Road Safety, VTI Report No., 399A, Swedish National Road and Transport Research Institute, 1995.

IXth PIARC International Winter Road Congress, Reprints from Technical Report, March 21-25, 1994, Seefeld, Austria, VTI Sartryck No. 214, 1994

Development of Anti-Icing Technology, SHRP-H-385, Transportation Research board, April, 1994

Handbook of Methods for Evaluating Chemical Deicers, SHRP-H-332, Transportation Research Board, November, 1992

Evaluation Procedures for Deicing Chemicals and Improved Sodium Chloride, SHRP-H-647, Transportation Research Board, June, 1993

Ice-Pavement Bond Disbonding — Fundamental Study, SHRP-H-643, Transportation Research Board, May, 1993

Ice-Pavement Bond Disbonding — Surface Modification and Disbonding, SHRP-DRAFT, Transportation Research Board.

An Improved Displacement Snowplow, SHRP-H-673, Transportation Research Board, March, 1994

Snow Fence Guide, SHRP-W/FR-91-106, Transportation Research Board, October, 1991

Alger, R.G., and J.P. Beckwith. A Comparison of Liquid and Solid Chemicals for Anti-Icing Applications on Pavements, TRB No. 940691, Transportation Research Board, 1994

Curtailing Usage of Deicing Agents in Winter, OECD Road Transport Research, 1989.

Use of Brine on Roads Results - Winter Season 1990-1991, Norwegian Public Road Administration, September, 1991

Berggeen, C.S. and P.H. Simonsen, Danish White Spot Program, Danish Road Directorate, 1985

Gustafson, Kent. Investigations of New Methods and Materials for Snow and Ice Control on Roads and Runways - MINSALT Project, Swedish Road and Traffic Research Institute, 1991

Gustafson Kent. Highway Snow and Ice Control, VTI Report 276A, Swedish Road and Traffic Research Institute, 1984

Proceedings of International Workshop on Winter Road Management, Organizing Committee of ITWWRM, March, 1993

Snow Removal and Ice Control Research, TRB Special Report 185, Transportation Research Board, 1979

Gray, D..M. and D. H. Hale. Handbook of Snow- Principles, Processes, Management and Use, University of Saskatchewan, 1981

Gustafson, Kent. Winter Maintenance - materials, Equipment and Procedures, Swedish Road and Traffic Research Institute, 1989

Kuemmel, D. A., Managing Roadway Snow and Ice Control Operations, NCHRP Project 20-5, Topic 23-03, (DRAFT), Transportation Research Board, January, 1993

Deicing Chemicals and Snow Control, Transportation Research Record 1157. Transportation Research Board, 1988

Highway Maintenance Operations and Research 1990, Transportation Research Record 1304. Transportation Research Board, 1991

French, K. A. and E.M. Wilson. Evaluation of the Potential of Remoter Sensing of Rural Road and Travel Conditions, Transportation Research Record 1409, Transportation Research Board, 1993

Transportation Research Record, No 1509, 1995

Hanbali, R. (1994). The Economic Impact of Winter Road Maintenance on Road Users, Paper No. 940191, presented at 73rd Annual Meeting of the Transportation Research Board, January 9-13, 1994, Washington DC.

Proceedings of the 7th Maintenance Management Conference, Transportation Research Board, 1995.

Transportation Research Circular, No. 447, 1995.

Nixon, W.A. (1993). Improved Cutting Edges for Ice Removal, SHRP Report No. H-346, National Research Council.

Nixon, W.A. and T.R. Frisbie, (1993). Field Measurements of Plow Loads During Ice Removal Operations: Iowa Department of Transportation Project HR334, IIHR Technical Report #365, 126 pages.

Nixon, W.A. and C.-H. Chung (1992). Development of a New Test Apparatus to Determine Scraping Loads for Ice Removal from Pavements, Proc. 11th IAHR Ice Symposium, vol. 1, pp. 116-127, Banff.

Rajorski, P., Dhar, S., and Sandhu, D. (1996). Forward Lighting Configurations for Snowplows, Paper No. 960783, presented at 75th Annual Meeting of the Transportation Research Board, January 7-11, 1996, Washington DC.

Wang, J.-Y., and Wright, J. R. (1994) Interactive Design of Service Routes, J. Transportation Engineering, ASCE, Vol. 120, No. 6, pp. 897 - 913.

Woodham, D. B. and Lacey, N.J. (1996). Real-Time Avalanche Detection and Location using Infrasound, Paper No. 960439, presented at 75th Annual Meeting of the Transportation Research Board, January 7-11, 1996, Washington DC.

Nixon, W.A. and Wei, Y.-C., "Snow Plow Cutting Edge Evaluation," South Dakota DOT Report No. SD95-14F, April 1996, 26 pages.

Nixon, W.A., Gawronski, T.J., and Whelan, A.E., "Development of a Model for the Ice Scraping Process: Iowa Department of Transportation Project HR 361," IIHR Technical report #383, October 1996.

Nixon, W.A. and Foster, N.S.J., "Strategies for Winter Highway Maintenance," University of Iowa Public Policy Center Report, November 1996.

Nixon, W.A. and Potter, J.D., "Measurement of Ice Scraping Forces on Snow-Plow Underbody Plows: Iowa Department of Transportation Project HR 372," IIHR Technical report #385, February 1997.

Appendix B: Snow and Ice Control Documents

The following documents are provided as examples of processes and procedures that can be used by roadway maintenance agencies. The documents are listed below.

Appendix B-1   Suggested Training Curriculum

Appendix B-2   Sample Contract for Snow and Ice Control Services

Appendix B-3   Sample Public Information Release

Appendix B-4   Spreader Calibration Procedures

Appendix B-5   Vehicle Maintenance Checklist

Appendix B-6   Examples of Materials Available from LTAP Centers

APPENDIX B-1
Suggested Curriculum Items for Snow and Ice Control Training Programs

I.　**POLICY**

　　A.　ADMINISTRATION AND MANAGEMENT
　　　　1.　Agency Snow and Ice Control Policies
　　　　2.　Snow and Ice Control Performance Guidelines
　　　　3.　Level of Service
　　　　4.　Snow and Ice Control Plan and Contingency Plans
　　　　5.　Cooperative Arrangements
　　　　6.　Contracts
　　　　　　a.　Snow and Ice Control
　　　　　　b.　Materials
　　　　　　c.　Equipment
　　　　　　d.　Special Services
　　　　　　e.　Maintenance and Repair
　　　　7.　Record Keeping
　　　　8.　Equipment Acquisition
　　　　9.　Materials Acquisition

　　B.　PERSONNEL/OPERATORS
　　　　1.　Personnel Policies
　　　　　　a.　Training requirements
　　　　　　b.　Certification
　　　　　　c.　Deployment
　　　　　　　　(1)　(Duty hours
　　　　　　　　(2)　(Standby
　　　　　　　　(3)　(Call-out
　　　　　　　　(4)　(Overtime
　　　　　　d.　Problem resolution
　　　　2.　Equipment/Clothing
　　　　3.　Training Programs
　　　　4.　Relationship with Other Agencies and Contractors

　　C.　CUSTOMER SERVICE
　　　　1.　Customer Oriented Work
　　　　　　a.　Define the Customer
　　　　　　b.　Customer Expectations
　　　　2.　Communicating with the Customers
　　　　3.　Cultivating and Communications with the Media

　　D.　LEGAL RIGHTS AND RESPONSIBILITIES

II.   PROCEDURES

A.   DECISION MAKING
    1.   Strategies and Tactics
        a.   Seasonal Preparation
        b.   Pre-storm/Event Preparation
        c.   Patrolling
        d.   Storm/Event Onset Operations
            (1)   Route Assignments
            (2)   Anti-icing
        e.   Operations During the Storm/Event
            (1)   Use of Chemicals
            (2)   Use of Abrasives
            (3)   Plowing techniques
        f.   Post Storm/Event Operations
        g.   Evaluation of Operations
    2.   Use of RWIS and Other Information Resources
        a.   Site-specific data
        b.   Forecasts
        c.   Ancillary data

B.   EQUIPMENT ISSUES
    1.   Vehicles
    2.   Storage
    3.   Maintenance
    4.   Cycle times
    5.   Safety Markings/Equipment
    6.   Types of Plows
    7.   Plow Blades/Cutting Edges

C.   EQUIPMENT MAINTENANCE
    1.   Vehicles
        a.   Routine
        b.   Preventive
        c.   Emergency
        d.   Pre- and Post Storm Operational Inspections
        e.   Post Season
    2.   Vehicle Attachments
        a.   Plows
        b.   Spreaders
    3.   Storage Facilities
    4.   Washing Facilities

E.   SNOW FENCES
    1.   Permanent (Constructed and Natural)
    2.   Temporary (Constructed and Natural)

III.   OPERATIONS

    A.   COMMUNICATIONS
        1.   Radio Policies and Procedures
        2.   Rules and Regulations
        3.   Do's and Don'ts
        4.   Dispatcher Procedures

    B.   PLOWING PROCEDURES
        1.   By LOS or Roadway Classification
        2.   Options for Various Lane Configurations
        3.   Special Situations
            a.   Bridges
            b.   Cul de Sacs, Alleys, Etc.
            c.   Wind Considerations
            d.   Snow Storage Considerations
            e.   Snow Disposal

    C.   MATERIAL APPLICATION PROCEDURES
        1.   Types of Materials Used
        2.   Types of Spreaders Used
        3.   Spreader Calibration
        4.   Spreader Controls
        5.   Getting the Application Rate Right

    D.   CLEANUP AND POST STORM CLEANUP

    E.   SAFETY GUIDELINES AND PROCEDURES
        1.   Training Requirements
        2.   Loading
        3.   Plowing
        4.   Spreading
        5.   Backing
        6.   Crossover
        7.   Disabled Agency Vehicles
        8.   Disabled Private Vehicles
        9.   Emergency Repairs
        10.   Cold Weather Hazards and Protection

    F.   ENVIRONMENTAL ISSUES WITH SNOW AND ICE CONTROL
        1.   Air and Water Quality
        2.   Vegetation
        3.   Structures and Pavements
        4.   Vehicles
        5.   Public Perception

IV.   STATE-OF-THE-ART SNOW AND ICE CONTROL

    A.   NEW TECHNOLOGY
        1.   Vehicles
        2.   Spreaders
        3.   RWIS
        4.   Communications

    B.   OTHER AGENCY PRACTICES
        1.   Local Agencies
        2.   State Agencies
        3.   International

V.   PRACTICUM (HANDS ON)

    A.   COMPUTER- OR GROUP-BASED TRAINING FOR DECISION MAKING

    B.   EQUIPMENT OPERATIONS
        1.   Plow Mounting
        2.   Plow operating
            a.   Front mount
            b.   Front mount with wing(s)
            c.   Underbody
        3.   Spreader mounting
        4.   Spreader operation
            a.   Calibration
            b.   Application rate
        5.   Snow Blower
        6.   Motor Grader
        7.   Loaders

    C.   Snow and Ice Control Materials
        1.   Chemicals
            a.   Dry
            b.   Liquid
            c.   Prewetting
            d.   Brine preparation
        2.   Abrasives
            a.   Mixing with chemicals
            b.   Prewetting

APPENDIX B-2
Sample Contract for Snow and Ice Control Services

The following contract was obtained from Virginia Department of Transportation. It is provided as an example only. As with all such documents, changes may have been made in later versions.

COMMONWEALTH OF VIRGINIA
DEPARTMENT OF TRANSPORTATION
NORTHERN VIRGINIA DISTRICT
FAIRFAX, VIRGINIA

DELIVER TO:
3975 Fair Ridge Drive
Fairfax, Virginia 22033
Receptionist, Terrace Level

MAIL TO:
3975 Fair Ridge Drive
Fairfax, Virginia 22033

INVITATION FOR BIDS - TERM CONTRACT

PURPOSE

The intent and purpose of this Invitation for Bids is to establish a contract with a qualified contractor to provide the commodity below to/for the Virginia Department of Transportation, herein referred to as VDOT. It is the Bidders responsibility to ensure that sealed bids in reposne to the Invitation for Bids are received at 1201 East Broad Street, 1st Floor, Richmond, Virginia prior to the due date and hour shown below at which time they will be publicly opened and read. Bids must be sealed, with commodity, bid number and opening date show on face of the envelop, including any special delivery envelopes.

Commodity: **SNOW REMOVAL OPERATIONS**

IFB#: MNV96SNR113-KLB

Authorized User: VDOT, Fairfax County

Contract Period: 10-1-96 through 9-30-98
Extendable one (1) additional year

VDOT Contact: K. L. Braxton, Contract
Administrator, Sr. (703) 934-7300

Date: July 11, 1996

Furnish Services in: Fairfax County
Fairfax County Parkway
Bid Due: 2:00 p.m. EDT; 08-08-96

Bid Opening: 10:00 a.m. EDT; 08-09-96

Technical Contact: L. E. Humphries
(703) 934-7300

In compliance with the above invitation and subject to all conditions imposed therein, the undersigned offers and agrees to furnish the services at the prices set in the pricing schedule. I certify that I am authorized to sign this bid for the bidder.

Company Name and Address
_____
_____
_____

Telephone Number _____

FAX # _____

Date: _____
By: _____
        Signature In Ink
Name: _____
        Please Print
Title: _____
FIN or SSN: _____
Female ( ) Yes ( ) NO
Minority ( ) Yes ( ) No

1

Commodity: Snow Removal Operations
IFB#: MNV96SNR113-KLB

TABLE OF CONTENTS

Commodity: Snow Removal Operations
IFB#: MNV96SNR113-KLB

PRICING SCHEDULE

PLEASE QUOTE PRICES FOR LOT(S) IN WHICH YOU ARE INTERESTED.

AWARD TO BE MADE ON EACH INDIVIDUAL LOT.

<u>LOT A:</u> Area 6: Between Beulah Street (Rt. 613) and Lee Chapel Road (Rt. 643)

<u>Item</u>	<u>Qty</u>	<u>Unit Price</u>	<u>Total Amount</u>
Mobilization	1 L.S.	_____	_____
Plow Rigging (# needed)	EA.	_____	_____
Stand by	HR.	_____	_____
Spreader Rigging (# needed)	EA.	_____	_____
Dump Truck w/ Spreader and Plow	EA.	_____	_____
Dump Truck w/ Plow only	EA.	_____	_____
Mechanic	HR.	_____	_____
Training/Orientation	300 HR.	_____	_____
Supervisor	HR.	_____	_____
	TOTAL (a)		_____

NUMBER OF TRUCKS TO BE SUPPLIED (b) ____

Contractors are required to submit prices on all items to be considered an acceptable bid.   Bid price for operators (drivers) shall be included in equipment bid price.

If the Contractor is unable to supply the total specified equipment, VDOT may accept more than one (1) bid to accomodate the required amount of equipment. However, the Contractor must be able to supply a minimum of twelve (12) trucks to be considered an acceptable bid.

Company Name and Address   Date: _____

_____   By: _____

_____   Name: _____
                                        Please Print

_____   Title: _____

3

Commodity: Snow Removal Operations
IFB#: MNV96SNR113-KLB

PLEASE QUOTE PRICES FOR LOT(S) IN WHICH YOU ARE INTERESTED.

AWARD TO BE MADE ON EACH INDIVIDUAL LOT.

<u>**LOT B:**</u> Areas 11, 4, and 3: Between Lee Chapel Road and the Dulles Toll Road

<u>Item</u>	<u>Qty</u>	<u>Unit Price</u>	<u>Total Amount</u>
Mobilization	1 L.S.	_____	_____
Plow Rigging (# needed)	EA.	_____	_____
Stand by	HR.	_____	_____
Spreader Rigging (# needed)	EA.	_____	_____
Dump Truck w/ Spreader and Plow	EA.	_____	_____
Dump Truck w/ Plow only	EA.	_____	_____
Mechanic	HR.	_____	_____
Training/Orientation	300 HR.	_____	_____
Supervisor	HR.	_____	_____
TOTAL (a)			_____

NUMBER OF TRUCKS TO BE SUPPLIED (b) _____

Contractors are required to submit prices on all items to be considered an acceptable bid. Bid price for operators (drivers) shall be included in equipment bid price.

If the Contractor is unable to supply the total specified equipment, VDOT may accept more than one (1) bid to accomodate the required amount of equipment. However, the Contractor must be able to supply a minimum of twelve (12) trucks to be considered an acceptable bid.

Company Name and Address   Date: _____

_____   By: _____

_____   Name: _____
                                                Please Print

_____   Title: _____

4

Commodity: Snow Removal Operations
IFB#: MNV96SNR113-KLB

I   SCOPE OF WORK

The Virginia Department of Transportation (VDOT) is soliciting bids from interested firms to furnish labor and equipment for snow removal operations within the Northern Virginia District in Fairfax County. This work will be performed on the **Franconia/Sprinfield Parkway** (between Beulah Street and I-95) and the **Fairfax County Parkway** (between I-95 and Sunset Hills Road). Work to be performed in accordance with the attached snow removal specifications.

Upon mutual agreement between VDOT and the Contractor, equipment may be utilized at other locations. The contractor(s) shall be totally responsible for snow and ice removal on the Franconia/Springfield Parkway and the Fairfax County Parkway.

II   GENERAL INFORMATION

For the purpose of this solicitation, each firm receiving this invitation for bid is referred to as a "Bidder" and the Bidder awarded the contract to supply the goods or services is referred to as a "Contractor". This invitation for bids states the instructions for submitting bids, the procedure and criteria by which a contract may be awarded, and the contractual terms which will govern the contract between VDOT and the Contractor.

III   AWARD OF CONTRACT

Award of contract will be determined on the lowest total cost offered by the lowest responsive, responsible bidder. VDOT reserves the right to reject any or all bids and waive technicalities as may be deemed to be in the best interest of the Commonweath. See additional reservations listed on the pricing schedule.

IV   TERMS OF CONTRACT

A.   Term of Contract:

The term of the contract shall be for one (1) year starting October 1, 1996 through September 30, 1998. The Department reserves the right to extend this contract for two (2) additional years in one (1) year intervals at the same terms, conditions and specifications at a price increased or decreased in accordance with paragraph b, if mutually agreeable and the Contractor has performed satisfactorily.

Commodity: Snow Removal Operations
IFB#:   MNV96SNR113-KLB

B.   **Price Increase/Decrease**

VDOT will consider price changes on additional period(s) provided they do not exceed the price(s) quoted in the original contract adjusted in accordance with the increase/decrease of the other services category of the CPI-W section of the Consumer Price Index of the United States Bureau of Labor Statistics for the previous twelve (12) months. Price changes may be permitted when factors affecting the market warrant and will be allowed only on the anniversary date of the contract. The Contractor should convey (in writing) its offer to extend the contract or raise/lower prices to the Virginia Departments of Transportation's Administrative Services Office no later then 60 days prior to the current contract term's expiration date. Applications for price changes shall be substantiated in writing with the request. VDOT shall have sole discretion in its decision to extend the contract or allow price changes.

V   **QUESTIONS CONCERNING THIS INVITATION FOR BID**

Any questions concerning this bid shall be directed to Ms. K. L. Braxton, Contract Administrator, Sr. at (703) 934-7300. For tehnical information, please contact Mr. L. E. Humphries at (703) 934-7300.

VI   **SPECIAL TERMS AND CONDITIONS**

A.   **Insurance:** The Contractor shall furnish a Certificate of Insurance showing the following insurance coverage are in force at the time the work commences, and that it will maintain these insurance coverages during the entire term of the contract. Additionally, all insurance must be provided by insurance companies authorized to sell insurance in Virginia by the Virginia State Corporation Commission. The certificate shall be furnished to VDOT within ten (10) calendar days after request. A thirty (30) day written notice of cancellation or nonrenewal shall be furnished to the Buyer identified in the solicitation at the address indicated. If the contractor fails to maintain the insurance required, VDOT may cancel the contract. The right is reserved to approve or reject the insurance provider, and notice of acceptance will be given by issuing a written purchase order.

6

Commodity: Snow Removal Operations
IFB#: MNV96SNR113-KLB

INSURANCE COVERAGES AND LIMITS REQUIRED

1. Worker's Compensation - statutory requirements and benefits.
2. Employers Liability - $100,000
3. General Liability - $500,000 combined single limit. The Commonwealth of Virginia is to be named as an additional insured with respect to the services being procured. The coverage is to include Premises/Operations Liability, Property Damage, Product and Completed Operators Coverage, Independent Contractor Liability, Owner's and Contractor's Protective Libility and Personal Injury Liability.
4. Automobile Liability - $500,000

VDOT reserves the right to approve or reject the insurance provider and will give notice of acceptance to the Contractor via a written purchase order.

B. **Bid Prices**

Prices quoted shall remain firm for the first one (1) year contract period. Adjustment for subsequent years if extended, may be made in accordance with Section IV, B.

C. **Payment**

Invoices are to be submitted on the 1st and the 15th of the month for all hours worked within the previous month. NO payment will be made for work in progress on the prescribed payment dates. Payment will be requested on forms provided by VDOT. Payments will be made within 30 days after receipt of completed payment request and verification of satisfactory completion of work.

D. **Cancellation of Contract**

VDOT reserves the right to terminate this contract for nonconformance of the contract. VDOT will meet with the Contractor to discuss any contract deficiencies and issue 10 days for the Contractor to take corrective action.

7

Commodity: Snow Removal Operations
IFB#:   MNV96SNR113-KLB

E.   Availability of Funds

It is understood and agreed between the parties herein that VDOT shall be bound hereunder only to the extent of the funds available or which may hereafter become available for the purpose of this agreement. The Contractor will be paid for all work performed, however, contract quantities may need to be adjusted.

F.   Performance and Payment Bonds

The successful bidder shall deliver to the Administrative Services Office, within 10 calendar days of notification of award, a duly executed Standard Performance and Payment Bonds (Form CO-10) payable to the Commonwealth of Virginia in the amount of 33 1/3 percent of the original contract award, as a guarantee for the faithful performance of the contract. The surety of the bond shall be a surety company approved by the State Corporation Commission to transact business in the Commonwealth of Virginia. No contract shall be deemed to be in effect until such bonds have been approved by the Administrative Services Office. Appropriate bond forms will be provided by the Administrative Services Office prior to award. In lieu of the performance and payment bonds, the successful bidder may furnish, in the face amount required for the bond, a certified check or cashier's check.

The following formula will be used in determining the performance and payment bond required:

{Total (A) / Total # Trucks} * # Trucks Supplied (b) = Bonding Amount

G.   Subletting

NO portion of this contract may be subcontracted without the written permission of the Engineer. Subcontractors must be fully qualified to perform the work and must adhere to all provisions of this contract. The prime contractor shall be fully responsible for the performance of all subcontracted work.

Commodity: Snow Removal Operations
IFB#: MNV96SNR113-KLB

H.   **Qualification Questionaire**

All bidders must complete the Vendor Qualification Questionaire (attachment c). Information provided will be used to help determine responsibility.

I.   **Claims**

The Contractor shall be responsible for resolution of any and all claims resulting from operators provided. Claims made to VDOT as a result of operators provided under this contract will be referred to the Contractor for handling. Failure to properly respond to and resolve property damage claims constitutes unsatisfactory performance and may result in cancellation of the contract.

J.   **Liquidated Damages**

For each hour delay after the prescribed time limit has expired that the Contractor's personnel have not been furnished, liquidated damages at the hourly rate per bid will be assessed.

SNOW REMOVAL GENERAL NOTES

The Virginia Department of Transportation (VDOT) is soliciting bids from interested firms to furnish labor and equipment for snow removal operations within the Northern Virginia District in Fairfax County at the following locations:

Franconia/Springfield Parkway (Route 7900)   Fairfax County Parkway (Route 7100)
Fr: Beulah Street (Route 613)   From: I-95
To: I-95   To: Sunset Hills Road (Route 675)

Contractor shall administer chemicals on roadway(s) as prescribed by the VDOT Engineer.

Contractor shall administer chemicals when snow is tracking or 1/4 inch has accumulated on the roadway(s). Contractor shall ensure that roadway(s) are passable to vehicles (using snow tires) at all times during snow storms.

Contractor shall ensure that bare pavement is achieved on roadway(s) 24 hours after completion of the storm. All intersections shall be opened and free of sight distance obstructions, snow is to be pushed back from shoulders and bridges and ramps cleared of snow and ice.

Commodity: Snow Removal Operations
IFB#: MNV96SNR113-KLB

SNOW REMOVAL SPECIFICATIONS

The Contractor shall provide equipment and operators in accordance with the terms and conditions outlined herein:

Contractor shall provide the minimum number of dump trucks for each lot as identified in the Pricing Schedule(s). All dump trucks shall be equiped with CB radios and/or other communication devices, snow plows and at least eight (8) cubic yard spreaders(tandem dump trucks). Contractor shall equip the trucks with liquid truck mounted spray units. All trucks must meet DMV requirements for licensed commercial vehicles. The Contractor shall be responsible for rigging of all trucks.

The Contractor must provide 100% of the dump trucks with plows and spreaders requested at the stated time to report to work. VDOT will provide at least four (4) hours notice.

The Contractor shall provide and keep operating at least 80% of the requested equipment during each snow operation. All equipment shall report to the headquarters fueled and in an operating condition.

The Contractor shall provide a mechanic to keep the equipment in working condition during the snow operations. The mechanic shall be capable of working on medium and heavy duty trucks as well as other snow equipment including VDOT equipment. Mechanics working on snow equipment must be approved by VDOT.

The Contractor shall provide a method of fueling the snow equipment on-site. The Contractor will be required to submit his method of fueling for approval by VDOT.

Contractor shall provide operators, with each dump truck, who possess a valid Commercial Drivers License to assist in emergency snow removal operations. All workers will be required to attend a short orientation and training session provided by VDOT at either a VDOT headquarters or the Contractor's complex. This training session shall be held at a time and date agreeable to both VDOT and the Contractor.

Contractor shall provide VDOT with a list of emergency numbers for weekend or night snow emergency operations to ensure the time provisions are met. This list shall contain company contact names and numbers.

Operators must be at least 18 years of age, capable of working nights and able to communicate. VDOT reserves the right to reject workers for not complying with these

Commodity: Snow Removal Operations
IFB#: MNV96SNR113-KLB

specifications. Operators shall be replaced at times and in a manner in which the truck does not leave the assigned work site.

The contractor shall provide one (1) supervisor with a vehicle, mobile phone and means of communicating with the dump trucks for each five (5) trucks provided.

Safety Standards

All personnel shall at all times wear approved clothing, safety vests, and any other equipment required to meet OSHA standards. They will obey all safety rules and regulations and will not create any hazardous conditions within the operation.

Failure to comply with safety requirements constitutes reason to restrict that operator from performing work under this contract.

Equipment

The contractor shall furnish all trucks, plows, spreaders, and liquid chloride tanks and any other attachments necessary to operate during the snow operations. All trucks shall be equiped with snow chains. Contractors' spreaders shall be equipped with liquid chloride tanks. The liquid chloride tank(s) shall have a minimum capacity of 140 gallons. The liquid spray injection system shall be capable of prewetting the materials from the spreader before being applied to roadway.

Prior to execution of contract ALL equipment shall be inspected by a VDOT representative, a Contractor's representative, and a VDOT mechanic. Any deficiencies shall be corrected within ten (10) calendar days.

Measurement and Payment

Mobilization will be paid in two installments. The first installment will be 25% of the bid item and paid once the contractor has successfully equipped all equipment with the appropriate hook ups to mount the assigned snow attachments. The second installment will be the remaining bid amount and will be paid at the end of the snow season, upon successful completion of the contract. The snow season will be officially over May 1 of each year.

The price for operators (drivers) shall be included in the equipment price. The Contractor will be paid the unit price for stand-by, once the equipment is signed-in, while waiting for snow operations and any other time the truck is participating in the snow operations but is not actually on the road. In the event the Contractor's equipment breaks down, no payment for that piece of equipment will be allowed until the equipment is back in an operating condition.

Commodity: Snow Removal Operations
IFB#: MNV96SNR113-KLB

equipment breaks down, no payment for that piece of equipment will be allowed until the equipment is back in an operating condition. The Contractor will be paid a minimum of four (4) hours at the stand-by rate for each piece of equipment ready for snow opertions.

The Following is a listing of the lots, estimated lane miles and amount of equipment needed in each area:

LOT A

Maint Area	Description	Lane Miles	Trucks w/ Plow & Spreaders	Trucks w/ Plow
006	Franconia/Springfield Parkway Fr: Beulah Street (Route 613) To: I-95 HOV Gates	0.79	2	2
006	Fairfax County Parkway Fr: I-95 HOV Gates To: Lee Chapel Rd. (Rt. 643)	36.8	4	4
	TOTAL LOT	37.59	6	6

LOT B

Maint Area	Description	Lane Miles	Trucks w/ Plow & Spreaders	Trucks w/ Plow
011	Fairfax County Parkway Fr: Lee Chapel Rd. (Rt. 643) To: Rt. 123 (includes ramps at Rt. 123)	20	3	3
011	Fairfax County Parkway Fr: Rt. 123 To: Fair Lakes Parkway (includes all ramps)	61.8	6	4
004	Fairfax County Parkway Fr: Rt. 50 To: Dulles Toll Road	30.3	4	4
	TOTAL LOT	112.1	13	11

Commodity: Snow Removal Operations
IFB#: MNV96SNR113-KLB
Attachment C

VENDOR QUALIFICATION QUESTIONAIRE

All vendors responding to this inquiry are required to complete this questionaire.

1   Name of Business _____

2   Type of Business (check one):

Proprietorship   _____
Partnership   _____
Corporation   _____

3   Name of Owner or Chief Executive Officer: _____
         Telephone Number: _____

4   How many years has the firm been in the business of providing the services called for in this inquiry? _____

5   How many persons are currently employed by the firm? _____

6   Provide a listing of equipment which will be used in performing the services required in this inquiry.

7   Is this equipment presently in the firm's equipment inventory? _____

8   What licenses or permits does the firm possess that are applicable to performing the services required? _____

9   Is the firm currently removed from a vendor list or debarred from doing business with any other Commonwealth of Virginia Agency? If yes, explain

_____

10   Provide the name, contact person and telephone number of three (3) customers which your firm has provided services of the same scope as those requested in this inquiry. These cutomers may be contacted as references:

Firm's Name	Contact Person	Telephone
_____	_____	_____
_____	_____	_____
_____	_____	_____

APPENDIX B-3
Examples of Snow and Ice Control Public Information

The following pages show examples of public information bulletins and press releases. All of the releases have been downloaded from the Internet. Many other examples can be found. For additional examples, access one of the common Internet search engines and type "snow and ice control."

Snow Removal Priority System

General Definition

The traffic volume handled by a road determines its priority for snow and ice removal. High-volume arteries such as Interstates, other four-lane highways and major state and federal routes receive first attention. Attention remains focused on these roads until they are cleared. Smaller secondary roads come next, again with traffic volume directing the priority. Residents along lightly traveled rural roads will often find that their road does not receive attention until after the storm has passed.

The Four Priority Categories

Roads in the state highway system are prioritized into four categories for the removal of snow and ice.

1. **First-priority routes are roads of major importance and high traffic volume which must be kept open to traffic at all times, regardless of cost. Roads in this category include Interstates, Appalachian Corridors and major urban connectors.**

2. **Second-priority routes are those only slightly less important than first-priority routes, such as school bus routes and primary roads not included in the first group. These routes are covered as quickly and as frequently as conditions will permit by the same equipment and personnel assigned to maintenance of first-priority routes.**

3. **Third-priority routes are of lesser importance due to traffic volume, construction and location. Required to be kept passable only for vehicles with tire chains, these roads receive attention only after all second-priority roads have been covered. Since these routes often receive attention only after a storm is over and are then kept passable only for traffic with chains, persons living along them should take necessary precautions.**

4. **Fourth-priority routes are state roads not essential to travel during snowstorms-- that is, roads not needed to provide citizens food, shelter or other essential needs. State park and forest roads are typical of fourth-priority routes that may be left uncleared for extended periods of time.**

Streets in Municipalities and Private Subdivisions

The Division of Highways is not responsible for clearing streets in towns and cities that are not part of the state system, nor does it usually maintain streets, lanes or roads in private subdivisions in unincorporated areas. To find out whether a road is on the state system and its priority category, you should contact your local county DOH office.

Return to <u>Winter Driving Center</u>

The cold facts of fighting snow and ice

When winter storms hit, WVDOT Division of Highways personnel are responsible for clearing all public roads in West Virginia with the exception of city-owned streets, which are the responsibility of the municipalities. In total, over 34,000 miles of roads fall under state responsibility.

- Print bits and sound bites
- Logistics
- Equipment
- Budget

- ***WVDOT** Winter Driving Information Center*

Print bits and sound bites

- 75,000 tons of salt and 132,000 tons of anti-skid materials such as sand and crushed stone are held ready for spreading in DOT stockpiles at 140 depot locations around the state.

- During a major statewide winter storm, Division of Highways snowplow trucks will log 150,000 miles a day.

- Daily expenses for fighting a major storm can hit $600,000. This battle can involve as many as 2,200 highway maintenance workers and 1000 snow-clearing vehicles.

- Highway crews will work 24 hours a day, in two 12-hour shifts, keeping the roads clear.

- An average of 121,000 tons of salt has been spread on the roads over each of the past six winters.

- Below 20 degrees Fahrenheit, salt rapidly loses its ice-melting power. During low temperature periods, alternative ice-melting chemicals may be required, but they are very expensive compared to salt.

- Over 5400 bolt-on snowplow blade edges were used in the past year. These carbide-tipped edges bolt onto the bottom of the plow blades and are the part that comes in contact with the road surface.

- Each October, snowplows around the state hit the road for dry runs. This practice allows operators to learn their routes, tune up the equipment and work out any unforseen problems.

Top of Page

Operations

Highway crews have to be ready to hit the road anytime the temperature drops to 35 degrees and precipitation is falling or predicted. When the air temperature hits freezing, any water on highway bridges will begin to turn to ice and must be treated with salt. Once the snow hits, snowplows must scrape the roads to remove the build-up, spread salt to melt the ice and spread sand or crushed stone to increase traction. In the midst of a statewide winter storm, DOH snowplows will log 150,000 lane-miles in a 24-hour day.

For safety and logistical purposes, all snowplowing trucks and graders are radio-equipped and drivers can communicate with their county offices at any time. All county offices are linked by radio to one of ten district control offices, which are in turn linked to the communications center at the State Capitol. This way, road and weather conditions can be monitored closely anywhere in the state.

Top of Page

Equipment

The DOH fleet includes two types of snowplow-equipped dump trucks: 529 single-axle and 88 tandem-axle vehicles. Single-axle trucks can carry five tons of salt and anti-skid materials and cost approximately $44,000 each. Tandem-axle trucks carry 12 tons of salt and anti-skid material and cost around $67,000 each. The larger tandem-axle snowplows are used almost exclusively on the Interstates and Appalachian Corridor expressways. Additionally, DOH utilizes about 150 graders and 220 end loaders to beef up the snow removal counter assault.

Back at the maintenance garages, other Highways workers are busy loading salt, refueling vehicles, staffing telephones and two-way radios and replacing worn snowplow blades. The bolt-on, carbide-tipped blade edges wear out from scraping pavement but are easily replaced. As a reserve, DOH will keep 1,500 of them in inventory and end up using several thousand a year.

Top of Page

Budget

$26 million is budgeted for snow and ice removal this winter. Actual expenditures for the past four winters were:

- 1995/96 $34.0 million
- 1994/95 $17.7 million
- 1993/94 $25.5 million
- 1992/93 $18.3 million

Prior to the winter of 92/93, the five-year average expenditure for snow removal and ice control was $12.3 million.

Top of Page

Salt Fact Sheet

A cost-effective highway deicer

Road salt is used to deice highways in West Virginia because it is effective and relatively inexpensive. With all the traffic, grades and curves on our roads, the use of salt is the only practical method available to keep our highways safe in winter. During winter weather conditions, public safety is always the first concern of the West Virginia Department of Transportation and its Division of Highways.

Salt, the mineral

Common road salt is sodium chloride (NaCl), a naturally occurring mineral found in seawater. It's what makes the oceans salty. Salt is found in large underground deposits which are the remains of ancient seas. Road salt and table salt are essentially the same, though road salt often has a special anti-caking agent added.

Quantities & capacities

At full capacity, WVDOT stockpiles hold about 73,000 tons of salt. This amount may be adequate for a very mild winter. During the average winter, however, around 100,000 tons will be used. A severe winter, such as 1993-94, can require the use of 140,000 tons or more. For deicing use during extremely cold periods, the state also keeps approximately 40,000 bags of calcium chloride on hand. In addition, over 100,000 tons of anti-skid materials (sand, crushed stone and cinders) are stockpiled. They are either mixed with salt or spread singularly on the road. These materials are purchased locally and their type varies based on price and availability. At all DOT storage areas, salt is stored in buildings or covered piles.

How salt melts ice

Water normally freezes at 32 degrees Fahrenheit, but salt lowers its freezing point. So at temperatures between 32 and the low 20s, salt effectively melts ice and snow. Daily temperature cycles common to West Virginia in winter usually include highs above 20 degrees, thus allowing salt to melt ice into water so that it can drain off the road.

Highway deicing during very cold periods

During very cold periods -- temperatures remaining below 20 degrees Fahrenheit -- salt alone will not effectively melt the ice. On busy Interstates, bridges and intersections, alternative ice melting chemicals may be used. Deicers such as calcium chloride will melt ice at lower temperatures than salt but are much more expensive to use. In these times, traction-boosting materials like sand, cinders and crushed stone will still be effective, and may be used alone.

Supply origin and shipping

Most salt used by the West Virginia Department of Transportation comes from mines in Louisiana and Texas. Salt vendors such as Morton International, Rochez and Cargill ship the rock salt up the Mississippi and Ohio rivers by barge to their storage depots in the region. Salt supplies for the Eastern Panhandle originate in New York and are shipped by rail to depots in Maryland. From the vendor depots, salt is delivered by truck to 140 DOT storage areas across state. The average delivered price of road salt is $35 per ton.

The salt industry

Highway deicing accounts for the majority of sodium chloride use in the United States. Nationally, a total of 31.5 million tons of salt was used in 1994 in the following major end-user percentages (according to The Salt Institute):

    59.8% Highway deicing
    8.7% Industrial processes
    8.2% Water conditioning
    6.3% Agriculture
    4.2% Human consumption

Winter Driving Center

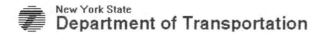

New York State
Department of Transportation

NYS DOT Press Release

IMMEDIATE

Michael Fleischer
(518) 457-6400

DOT's HIGH-TECH WONDERLAND

(Albany, New York - December 17, 1996) Winter doesn't start, officially, until 9:06am on December 21st, but many in the State have already seen a preview of what is to come. In an average year, nearly 120 inches of snow blankets the 110,000 miles of roadways across New York State.

State Transportation Commissioner John B. Daly noted, "With the technological explosion of the past decade, snow and ice control is going high-tech. Advanced weather tracking and forecasting systems team up with state-of-the-art sensing equipment to help DOT clear and de-ice roadways faster, and more efficiently, making roadways safer for the traveling public."

With help from the State Department of Transportation, local governments maintain snow and ice control on 95,000 miles of streets and highways, DOT itself clears about 15,000 miles. Keeping the roads open for winter travel takes accurate forecasting, a fleet of over 1,300 trucks, over half a million tons of salt, 600,000 tons of sand and more than 4,000 dedicated men and women.

Salt, sand and plowing remain the major weapons against snow and ice. Salt melts snow and prevents it from bonding to the pavement which would create a hard pack layer that is difficult to remove. Salt, as an ice melter, is more effective when used at pavement temperatures above 15 degrees. Sand is generally used at temperatures lower than 15 degrees and on steep grades where there is no time to wait for the melting action of salt.

All the Department's 1,300 snow and ice trucks are equipped with automatic ground speed controls that assure the proper distribution of salt and sand mixtures on the roadways. Manual systems required the plow operator to drive at a constant rate of speed to maintain an even application. The automatic system senses stops and starts and adjusts the rate of release to the trucks speed. The use of micro-processors has made the automatic systems more accurate and reliable. Since 1990, all new DOT trucks have specified micro-processor-controlled distribution systems.

Commissioner Daly announced, "The Department is piloting a new state-of-the-art zero-velocity spreader. This new equipment spreads sand and salt at a velocity equal to the speed of the truck, greatly reducing bounce and scatter. The Department has been working to achieve the same effect for a number of years but expects to find this new device more effective than methods tried in the past. This new equipment will be field tested in the Department's Rochester region, historically known for its heavy snows. Salt remains the most effective tool to combat the elements, however the Department anticipates spreading less salt and sand when using this device."

Accurate weather forecasting is essential for DOT's snow and ice crews. DOT utilizes a number of new technologies including weather radar, road weather information systems (RWIS) and hand held pavement temperature sensors.

Real-time weather radar and satellite imagery provides DOT storm managers with valuable information on storm timing, assisting them in making critical decisions on deployment of crews and the type and timing of treatments. These critical decisions help DOT both control costs and increase the effectiveness of its operations.

RWIS provide computerized site specific weather and road data. RWIS technology was developed in Europe then introduced to the United States in the mid-eighties. Pavement sensors provide real-time data on the temperature, moisture and chemical content of the pavement surface, whereas atmospheric sensors (thermister, anemometer, wind direction indicator, hygrometer and precipitation sensors) provide weather details. A remote processing unit, located on a roadside or bridge, collects data from sensors and sends it to a central processing unit. A central clearing house then analyzes the data and prepares site specific pavement temperature and climatic forecasts.

Because of its aggressive pursuit of Roadway Weather Information Systems, New York State has been named a national lead State in the implementation of this technology. With this designation New York is expected to provide leadership and technical assistance to States nationwide in the implementation of tools and techniques for this evolving technology.

Commissioner Daly noted, "This improved technology, however, is only as good as the skilled crews that utilize it." Negotiating a 23-ton snowplow through commuter traffic and winding roadways is difficult even in the best of conditions. Driving one in blinding snow and on icy highways takes a great deal of skill and alertness. These skills are sharpened during hours of classroom and behind-the-wheel training. Those skills are further honed in DOT's statewide and regional snowfighting schools.

Commissioner Daly said, "The Department's highly trained snow and ice crews are among the best in the country."

Commissioner Daly reminds all drivers, "Give snow-fighting crews room to work, do not follow too closely. DOT snow crews go through extensive, rigorous training but the fact remains, plow trucks carry a lot of equipment, so they do have blind spots where the driver can't see you, especially in the rear. Do not pass...snow plows drive at speeds safe for road conditions. Remember, the road behind the plow has been cleared and is safer."

DOT crews will be out in force on State roadways clearing snow and ice, but sophisticated technology and skilled workers cannot make winter driving completely safe, motorists must do their part. Adjusting your driving to conditions is one of the best safety measures possible.

DRIVE CAUTIOUSLY! Don't be daring. Adjust your speed for road conditions and leave extra time, it will be slow-going out there. Keep a longer following distance between you and the car in front of you. It will take you longer to stop your car on snow or ice covered roads, tap the brakes and change direction gradually.

Assume that bridge surfaces are slippery. Bridges freeze more quickly than road surfaces because their undersides are exposed to the cold temperatures.

During periods of snow, rain, sleet or fog, turn on your headlights so that other motorists can see you...it's the law in New York.

Keep your windshield, windows and mirrors clear of ice, snow and condensation.

Commissioner Daly advises motorists, "Keep this winter season a safe one. Stay alert behind the wheel and adjust your driving to road and weather conditions, and always drive defensively."

Print, radio and television on location interviews are invited. Contact Susan O'Connor (518)457-6400.

96-70

NY State Department of Transportation
Information Management Bureau
Last Update: December 19, 1996

Winter Maintenance Overview

The upcoming winter months bring a changed focus in the level of responsibility for Department of Transportation maintenance crews. Snow and ice control equipment and operators are on call 24 hours a day in order to be able to address winter road conditions in a timely manner. As in past years, WSDOT Maintenance crews will work in partnership with the Washington State Patrol relative to conditions along the highways.

In Northeastern Washington, state highway snow removal is handled by maintenance crews under the jurisdiction of D.O.T./Eastern Region. The region encompasses seven counties: Adams, Ferry, Lincoln, Spokane, Stevens, Pend Oreille, and Whitman. There are 1,577 centerline miles of state highways within the Eastern Region boundaries. To keep the roads clear and safe for travel, the WSDOT uses over 100 pieces of equipment in the Eastern Region. Most of these vehicles are combination snowplow/sander trucks. Maintenance crews and equipment are based in Spokane, Colfax, Colville, and Davenport with additional equipment sheds located at strategic points throughout the region.

This winter season brings some new challenges to the Eastern Region—snow and ice operations. Financial and workforce limitations necessitate achieving greater efficiencies in the snow removal/ice control program. The program and associated decisions determine the frequency of snow removal and ice control on state highways based on the functional class of the various highway sections

Average daily traffic counts determine the functional class of a state highway and its position in the snow and ice priority list. Urban freeways and primary arterials receive the greatest emphasis in this program followed by rural facilities. Rural collector highways have the lowest priority. Each section of highway in the Eastern Region has been assigned a frequency of service for snow and ice attention

Also, snow removal and ice control efficiency is related directly to staffing levels and the ability to keep equipment in use on the highway. The Eastern Region will primarily rely on existing permanent staff for snow and ice control. The hiring of temporary personnel serving on an "on-call" basis will be done to augment the winter highway coverage only when severe conditions dictate additional needs. Although more economical than staffing maintenance facilities 20 to 24 hours per day, this "on-call" process can result in longer response times to problem areas during severe weather conditions

During the winter season, there are many times when the snow is falling faster than the plows can clear the highways. When this occurs, the cold snow bonds to the warm pavement and is packed down by passing vehicles. This "compact snow and ice" condition can be very treacherous and motorists are advised to lower their speed accordingly. When the snow becomes compacted, plows are unable to remove it completely from the roadway. Traction sand is then applied to the highway surface to make the road more passable. Crews will concentrate sand distribution at intersections, curves, on bridge surfaces, and hills under most conditions

In the Spokane area, air quality continues to be an important issue and dust from traction sand on the roadway is a major concern. To control that dust, traction sand is now removed from the roadway during dry periods, especially along Interstate 90. These efforts are helping the community avoid violations of the PM10 regulations that are now in effect in Spokane County

Motorists who are planning winter travel should be aware of changing weather and road conditions and carry emergency equipment such as tire chains, warm blankets, extra clothes, flashlight, first aid kit, etc. Information on all mountain passes in Washington State is available from the Department of Transportation by calling the toll-free number (888)SNO-INFO (766-4636

Snow and Ice Control

The Department of Streets and Sanitation is in charge of keeping Chicago's streets free of ice and snow during inclement winter weather. Radar and a variety of professional weather services are used to anticipate the approach of snow or freezing rain. When such weather nears Chicago, the city dispatches some or all of its 280 salt spreaders/plows to the main arterial streets which are divided into 245 routes.

City crews also salt/plow Lake Shore Drive and the Chicago Skyway toll bridge, but the city's expressways themselves are under the jurisdiction of the Illinois Department of Transportation. The salt used by the city is ordinary rock salt. The salt is sometimes treated with the additive calcium chloride when needed to enhance the effectiveness of the road salt in below-zero temperatures; calcium chloride is routinely used on Lake Shore Drive so as to use less salt and better protect the foliage along Lake Michigan's shore.

Some 607 miles of arterial streets are permanently designated as *snow routes* that automatically restrict parking whenever there are at least two inches of snow on the pavement. Among these streets are the 107 miles of priority arterials that also restrict parking every day from 3 a.m. to 7 a.m. between December 1 and April 1 regardless of whether snow is present. Both of these parking bans were implemented to prevent recurrences of 1967 and 1979 when Chicago came to a traffic standstill due to major snowstorms.

Whenever the arterial streets are deemed safe for travel during or after a snowfall, the city's salt trucks are dispatched to the secondary, residential streets for salting and plowing operations. This work continues until all city streets have been treated.

For major snowstorms, Streets and Sanitation also has the capacity to equip several hundred garbage trucks with "quick hitch" plows to supplement the salt truck fleet. In addition, heavy equipment and labor are available from other municipal departments and the private sector for snow clearance during and after a full-fledged blizzard.

In February 1994, Chicago received nearly two feet of snow within a 60-hour period--the most significant blizzard since 1979. Streets and Sanitation put 700 pieces of equipment on the streets, which were getting snow at the rate of one inch every 30 minutes. In contrast to 1979, the Blizzard of 1994 failed to close any Chicago streets due to the availability of more equipment and better planning than existed 15 years earlier.

Chicago averages 39 inches of snow annually. While snowfall officially is registered at O'Hare International Airport northwest of the city's corporate limits, there often are higher accumulations along the eastern edge of the city due to "lake effect" snowfalls created by the effect of Lake Michigan on meteorological conditions.

Streets & Sanitation

Directory of City Services

Home Page

APPENDIX B-4
Calibration Procedures (from The Salt Institute's Snow Fighter's Handbook)

Different materials will spread at differ-ent rates at the same setting, so spreaders must be calibrated with the material that will be used.

Spreader Calibration Procedure

Calibration of spreaders is simply calculating the pounds per mile discharged at various spreader control settings and truck speeds by first counting the number of auger or conveyor shaft revolutions per minute, measuring the salt discharged in one revolution, then multiplying the two and finally multiplying the discharge rate by the minutes it takes to travel one mile.

With hopper-type spreaders, specific gate openings must be calibrated. Measure from floor of conveyor to bottom edge of gate.

Each spreader must be calibrated individually; even the same models can vary widely at the same setting.

Equipment needed:

1. Scale for weighing.
2. Canvas of bucket/collection device.
3. Chalk, crayon or other marker.
4. Watch with second hand.

CALIBRATION CHART

Agency: _____
Location: _____
Truck No.: _____ Spreader No.: _____
Date: _____ By: _____

GATE OPENING (HOPPER TYPE SPREADERS)			POUNDS DISCHARGED PER MILE								
A	B	C	MINUTES TO TRAVEL ONE MILE								
Control Setting	Shaft RPM (Loaded)	Discharge Per Revolution (Pounds)	Discharge Rate (Lbs/Min	5 mph x 12.00	10 mph x 6.00	15 mph x 4.00	20 mph x 3.00	25 mph x 2.40	30 mph x 2.00	35 mph x 1.71	40 mph x 1.50	45 mph x 1.33
1												
2												
3												
4												
5												
6												
7												
8												
9												
10												

Calibration steps:

1. Warm truck's hydraulic oil to normal operating temperature with spreader sys-tem running.
2. Put partial load of salt on truck.
3. Mark shaft end of auger or conveyor.
4. Dump salt on auger or conveyor.
5. Rev truck engine to operating RPM (at least 2000 RPM).
6. Count number of shaft revolutions per minute at each spreader control set-ting, and record.
7. Collect salt for one revolution & weigh, deducting weight of container. (For greater accuracy, collect salt for several revolutions and divide by this number of turns to get the weight for one revolution.) This can be accomplished at idle or very low engine RPM.
8. Multiply shaft RPM (Column A) by discharge per revolution (Column B) to get discharge rate in pounds per minute (Column C), then multiply discharge rate by minutes to ravel one mile at various truck speeds to get pounds discharged per mile.*

Calibrating Automatic Controls

Automatic controls come with factory calibration cards that indicated the proper rate of spread for each setting. However, when there is a need to calibrate, use the following steps:

1. Remove or turn off spinner.
2. Set auger on given number, such as No. 2.
3. Tie sack or heavy canvas under discharge chute.
4. Mark specific distance, such as 100 or 1,000 feet.
5. Drive that distance with spreader operating.
6. Weigh salt collected in sack or canvas.
7. Multiply weight of salt by 5.2 (in case of 1,000 feet) or 52.8 in case of 100 feet).

This will be the amount of salt discharged per mile, which remains constant regardless of speed, but calibration must be done for each control setting.

---

* For example, at 20 MPH with 30 Shaft RPM and 7 lbs. discharge— 30 x 7 = 210 x 3.00 = 630 lbs. per mile.

APPENDIX B-5- SAMPLE VEHICLE CHECKLIST
(from the Minnesota DOT Operator's Vehicle Daily Preventive Maintenance Checklist)

OPERATOR'S VEHICLE DAILY PREVENTIVE MAINTENANCE

Station/Garage_____   Unit # _____

Mileage_____   Date_____

Each unit, when used, will be checked daily, and this report turned in to immediate supervisor at the end of each pay period or weekly for 3-month file retention. Units classified as commercial vehicles shall retain previous day's checklist or copy as well as current day's checklist.

Pre-Operational Check:	X	Remarks:	R
• Pintle hitch or 5th Wheel			
• Steering Mechanism			
• Horn			
• Mirrors			
• Windshield Wiper/Washer			
• Tires			
• Wheel Nuts, Rims			
• Emergency Equipment			
• Service Brake (Incl. Trailer brakes and connections)			
• Parking Brake			
• Lights and Reflectors Broken or Obscured			
Unit Cleanliness			
Heater/Defroster			
Fluid Leaks			
Visual Inspection (tires, body damage, glass)			
Engine Oil			
Cooling System			
Power Steering Fluid			
Engine Belts			
Battery and Cables			
Air Guard Fluid			
Drain Air Tanks			
Grease Spring & Box Pins			
Hydraulic Fluid Level			
Plow & Wing Cutting Edge			
Sander Bearings & Chain			
Body Damage (dents, scratches, glass):		Describe on back	

SIGNED:

   (Operator) _____

Reviewed by Supervisor: _____

This list includes the basic items that must be checked daily as a form of habit and in no way restricts or limits checking other items. As this form is to be used for cars, pickups, all classes of trucks, and other mobile equipment, there will be some items that may not apply. "Certain vehicles (agency dependent)" need only be checked when fueling the unit.

Deficiencies that cannot be corrected by the OPERATOR are to be reported to the SHOP SUPERVISOR immediately on Form X in the Unit Service Book.

Mark "X" for any item needing repair. Mark "R" for repair if request has been made to shop. Mark "✓" for items in serviceable condition.

Items with an X notation must be deadlined if they meet State Police/Patrol criteria for deadlining a vehicle.

APPENDIX B-6
Examples of Materials Available from LTAP Centers

LTAP Materials Related to Training

Plow Power, produced: 1987 by the New England Chapter of American Public Works Association. This video shows the proper techniques for residential and local highway plowing. Actual plowing scenes depict the use of one-way, reversible, wing and tandem plowing procedures for roads and cul-de-sacs. Responsibility to the public and safety issues are stressed. Target audience: Snow plow drivers and other operations personnel;

Response to Winter, produced in 1993 by the Pennsylvania Department of Transportation. It describes the how and why of Pennsylvania Department of Transportation's winter operations. Target audience: Supervisors and work crews

White Gold, produced by the New England Chapter of American Public Works Association. This video stresses the proper selection and operation of equipment for snow and ice operations. Topics include: storm preparation; weather forecasting; storm center operations; snow plowing; cutting edge selection; proper mounting of snow plows on equipment; power trains; advantages of various sanding equipment; use of pickup trucks in snow removal operations; snow removal from downtown areas; and sidewalk plowing. Target audience: Public works directors

LTAP Materials Related to Liability and Snow and Ice Control

Extra Eyes on Maintenance. Product: Videocassette, 32 minutes. Date produced: 1988. Source: Pennsylvania Department of Transportation
Description: This videocassette shows how everybody can help maintenance workers reduce the chances of a tort suit. (AV#00734). Target audience: Supervisors, workers

Risk Management and Minimizing Tort Liability for Local Highway Departments. Product: Manual (108 pages) includes index. Date produced: 1989. Source: Cornell Local Roads Program
Description: This training manual was originally developed for a training course on risk management and tort liability taught in New York State. The manual serves as a basic reference publication on principles of risk management and tort liability suitable for highway and public works officials and others responsible for maintaining and managing public highways. Course has also been taught in Nevada and Idaho. (CLRP Report #91-10). Target audience: Highway and public works officials

Risk Management to Reduce Highway Tort Liability. Product: Course (24 hours). Date produced: 1990. Source: Transportation Training Division, Texas Engineering Extension Service.
Description: This course covers the key concepts of risk management, and activities related to potential and actual law suits, including pre-trial, trial, and post-trial activities. The course includes a mock trial workshop. Target audience: Personnel responsible for road design, construction, maintenance and attorneys

Risk Management: Tort Litigation. Product: Videocassette, 20 minutes. Date produced: 1984. Source: Pennsylvania Department of Transportation.
Description: This videotape covers involvement in tort claims and is designed to outline in easy-to-understand terms and concepts the things that get us, as a department, involved in tort claims. It also describes methods to avoid such claims. The videotape follows a new assistant county manager as he is briefed on risk management procedures. (AV#00681). Target audience: Managers, engineers, and clerical staff.

Roadway Management and Tort Liability in Wisconsin. Product: Fact sheet. Date produced: 1990. Source: Wisconsin Transportation Information Center
Description: This fact sheet discusses tort liability in Wisconsin and its development as a result of court rulings. It also presents recommendations for administrative and roadway management practices. Some suggestions for developing local policy are given, in specific areas, which can help reduce exposure. Target audience: Local roads staff and elected officials.

Safety Program. Product: Publications. Date produced: 1991- present. Source: Various.
Description: The Safety Program is a set of materials to help provide safety education and awareness. It includes safety brochures and bulletins and question and answer sheets addressing various aspects of safety, including traffic safety, worker safety and pedestrian safety. Additional materials are issued bi-monthly. Target audience: County judges, mayors, public works directors, road supervisors and transportation coordinators, local officials, media, schools

Tort Liability for Maintenance. Product: Videocassette (VHS). Date produced: 1991. Source: Louisiana Transportation Research Center.
Description: This videocassette provides an introduction to transportation-related tort liability. It covers the seriousness of the problem, Department of Transportation and Development's responsibilities, legal terms, an explanation of present laws, summaries of pertinent court cases with an explanation of who was held accountable and why, and how to prevent or correct the problem. (M7025A). Target audience: Maintenance administrators, supervisors and crews.

Appendix C:
Sample Material and
Equipment Specifications

The following documents are provided as examples of specifications that can be used by roadway maintenance agencies. Each is subject to change and the agencies that originated them should be contacted for the latest versions. Appendix C-2 is the property of the Pacific Northwest States. This document has been reformatted for inclusion in this Guide.

The documents are listed below.

Appendix C-1   New York State DOT Bid Specification for Salt

Appendix C-2   Pacific Northwest States Snow and Ice Control Chemical Specification

Appendix C-3   Liquid Deicer Application Equipment, Sander Unit Specification

Appendix C-4   Pre-wetting Application System Specification

APPENDIX C-1
Detailed Specification for Ice Control Salt

The following bid specification for road salt has been provided by and is reprinted with the permission of the New York State Department of Transportation. It is provided as an example only.

STATE OF NEW YORK
DEPARTMENT OF TRANSPORTATION

1997-98 ROAD SALT REQUIREMENTS

General Bid Provisions
and Detailed Specifications
(Specification #97-026)

Invitation for Bids #BA-026 - Bid Opening of August 8, 1997

(a) The contractor will not discriminate against employees or applicants for employment because of race, creed, color, national origin, sex, age, disability or marital status, and will undertake or continue existing programs of affirmative action to ensure that minority group members and women are afforded equal employment opportunities without discrimination. For purposes of this article, affirmative action shall mean recruitment, employment, job assignment, promotion, upgradings, demotion, transfer, layoff or termination, and rates of pay or other forms of compensation.

(b) At the request of the contracting agency, the contractor shall request each employment agency, labor union, or authorized representative of workers with which it has a collective bargaining or other agreement or understanding, to furnish a written statement that such employment agency, labor union or representative will not discriminate on the basis of race, creed, color, national origin, sex, age, disability or marital status, and that such union or representative will affirmatively cooperate in the implementation of the contractor's obligations herein.

(c) The contractor shall state in all solicitations or advertisements for employees, that, in the performance of the State contract, all qualified applicants will be afforded equal employment opportunities without discrimination because of race, creed, color, national origin, sex, age, disability or marital status.

Contractor will include the provisions of "a", "b", and "c" above, in every subcontract over $25,000 for the construction, demolition, replacement, major repair, renovation, planning or design of real property and improvements thereon (the "Work") except where the work is for the beneficial use of the Contractor. Section 312 does not apply to: (i) work, goods, or services unrelated to this contract; or   (ii) employment outside New York State; or   (iii) banking services, insurance policies or the sale of securities. The State shall consider compliance by a contractor or subcontractor with the requirements of any federal law concerning equal employment opportunity which effectuates the purpose of this section. The contracting agency shall determine whether the imposition of the requirements of provisions hereof duplicate or conflict with such federal law, and if such duplication or conflict exists, the contracting agency shall waive the applicability of Section 312 to the extent of such duplication or conflict. Contractor will comply with all duly promulgated and lawful rules and regulations of the Governor's Office of Minority and Women's Business Development pertaining hereto.

NOTICE TO BIDDERS

1. Sealed bids for the furnishing and delivery of the materials, equipment or services as specified in this Invitation for Bids, will be received by the Procurement Bureau, New York State Department of Transportation, 1220 Washington Avenue, Albany, NY 12232-0201, until the date and time indicated on the cover sheet, when they will be publicly opened and read.

2. All Proposals should be submitted in the envelope furnished. All the required information should be recorded on the envelope containing the proposal. In the event a bidder fails to provide such information, DOT Procurement Personnel reserve the right to open the envelope to determine the proper Proposal number, and the time and date of the Bid Opening. The opening of such bid shall not affect the validity of same.

3. All bids are to be submitted on the forms provided by the State.

4. Appendix A, standard clauses for all New York State contracts, is attached hereto, and is hereby made a part of any resulting agreement as if set forth fully herein. No bid will be considered for award unless it includes Appendix A as part of the bid.

5. This sheet is considered to be a part of the proposal and of any contract relating thereto.

6. All quantities in the bid are subject to overrun or underrun not to exceed 20% at the discretion of the Department of Transportation.

7. On all bid documents, the words "or equal" are understood to apply where a brand name, trade name, catalog reference or patented commodity is referenced, unless otherwise stated.

8. Cash discount will not be considered in determining low bidder, but discounts of 1% or greater will be taken into consideration in awarding tie bids.

9. Bids received later than the date and time specified will not be considered and will be returned to bidder unopened, unless satisfactory timely bids were not received.

10. Amendments to or withdrawals of bids, received later than the date and time of bid opening will not be considered, however, a bidder who has already been declared the low bidder may further reduce its price. Any or all proposals may be rejected.

11. Prices and information required by the Bid Proposal should be typewritten or printed in ink for legibility. All signatures must be written in ink.

12. Delivery shall be expressed in number of calendar days after receipt of a purchase order. Guaranteed delivery may be considered in making award under certain circumstances.

13. A bidder may submit alternate proposals containing deviations in detailed specifications, contract period, quality, etc. Bidder shall state in detail wherein it differs from the terms of the invitation for bids and specifications as issued, and consideration may be given to any or all such differences provided such action is in the best interest of the state.

14. Purchases made by the State of New York are not subject to state or local sales taxes or federal excise taxes. There is no exemption from paying the New York State truck mileage, unemployment insurance, or Federal Social Security taxes. The official State Agency purchase order is sufficient evidence to qualify the transaction exempt from sales tax under section 116(a)(1), Tax Law. For free transactions under the Internal Revenue Code, the New York State registration number is 14740026K.

15. The State shall have the right to terminate any resulting contract upon thirty days written notice to the Contractor. However, in the event of Contractor default, the contract may be terminated with or without prior notice.

16. The accounts of the Contractor shall clearly identify the costs of the work performed under an awarded contract and shall be subject to audit within three years of the completion date, by the State, and on Federally Aided Projects, by the Federal Highway Administration.

17. If, subsequent to award of a contract as a result of a Proposal submitted in response to this Invitation for Bids, the Contractor shall fail to perform satisfactorily, the State shall reserve the right, upon termination for cause, to obtain the required goods or services from other sources with or without formally bidding. For all such purchases of replacement goods or services, the Contractor held in default shall be liable for, and shall promptly reimburse the State upon request, for any and all additional costs incurred.

METHOD OF AWARD

Award will be made by **grand total bid price per zone**. Some zones may have requirements both for "Bulk delivery to State sheds" and "Built into stockpiles and covered by Contractor". Award on these zones will be by the Total Zone Bid for both types of delivery.

The right is reserved to limit the total quantity awarded to one contractor if, in the opinion of the Director of Procurement, such contractor may be unable to fulfill the contract commitment. In such an event, the decision of the State to award in its best interest shall be appealable in writing to the Director within ten calendar days of rendering of such a decision. Bidder is not entitled to such an option unless detailed in the bid, or in an attachment to the bid prior to the Bid Opening.

In the event of tie bids, award shall be made in whatever manner is most advantageous to the State, at the discretion of the Director of Procurement. The State reserves the right to reject any or all bids for cause.

BIDDING

Price Computation Worksheets (attachment 1) have been provided for your use in calculating your best bid price. It is not necessary to return the worksheets with your bid. Return only the separate Invitation for Bids,   WHICH CONSTITUTES YOUR BID AND MUST BE RETURNED. All stockpile locations within any one zone are to be bid as one price. An updated Zone Map is included in Attachment 1.

CONTRACT PERIOD

The contract period shall be for a period of eight months, effective from September 15, 1997 through May 14, 1998. The contract may be extended, either in whole or in part, for up to two additional eight month periods under identical terms and conditions (except for quantities, which are subject to change) upon mutual agreement. Unit Prices are subject to adjustment as per the **Economic Price Adjustment Clause** below. "In part," as used herein, shall be defined as meaning individual zones.

file: salt97.026

ECONOMIC PRICE ADJUSTMENT

The unit prices of all items listed in any Notice of Contract Award resulting from this solicitation are subject to price adjustment at the time any extension option is exercised, either upward or downward by application of one of the formulas set forth below. The indexes to be used in the computation of the price adjustment(s) shall be

(a) Chemical and Fertilizer Mining - (Rock Salt [Product Code 1479-3]);
(b) Local Trucking without Storage - (Dump Trucking [Product Code 4212-3]);
(c) Railroads, Line Haul Operating - (Non-Metallic Minerals [Product Code 4011-A04]);
(d) Deep Sea Foreign Transportation of Freight - (Inbound Services [Product Code 4412-1]);
(e) Freight Transportation on the Great Lakes - St. Lawrence Seaway (Self Propelled Dry Bulk Cargo Vessel Service [Product Code 4432-111])

as quoted in the Producer Price Index as published by the U.S. Department of Labor, Bureau of Labor Statistics under "net output of selected industries and their products, not seasonally adjusted".

The indexes published for the month of April, 1997 shall be used as the base index for determining price adjustments. The indexes for the month(s) of April, 1998 and April, 1999 shall be used in determining the adjusted contract price(s).

Whenever a price adjustment is made pursuant to this clause, the indexes which were used for computing the adjustment shall become the new base index for determining further adjustments. Adjustments will only be made upon extension of the contract period as provided for under 'Contract Period' above. The *aggregate* of any *increase* in unit prices under this clause shall not exceed ten percent. There is no limitation on the percentage of *decrease* made under this clause.

Price Adjustment Formulas:

For purposes of price adjustment calculation, the index for Rock Salt (Product Code 1479-3) shall constitute one-half of the total adjustment, and transportation cost shall constitute the other half.

Further, Local Trucking (Product Code 4212-3) shall always be considered the *Primary* method of transportation. Where a bidder has not designated a *Secondary* method of transportation, Local Trucking shall constitute the entire transportation adjustment.   However, where a bidder designates in its bid, a secondary method of transportation, both the primary and secondary methods shall constitute one-half of the total transportation adjustment.

One of the following formulas will govern price adjustment under this clause:

1) Where a secondary method of transportation *has not* been designated, the adjustment shall be computed based upon the change in (a) X .50 + the change in (b) X .50.

2) Where a secondary method *has* been designated, the adjustment shall be computed based upon the change in (a) X .50 + the change in (b) X .25 + the change in either (c), (d), or (e) as appropriate, X .25.

See end of Bid to designate a secondary method of Transportation.

QUANTITIES

The quantities listed are estimates based on filed requirements. Each contract, however, shall be for the quantities actually ordered during the contract period (see Guaranteed Minimum Purchase and Maximum Delivery Quantity). Contractors are required to supply all quantities ordered, consistent with maximum and minimum quantities established herein.

A) Guaranteed Minimum Purchase

Notwithstanding the 'Guaranteed Early Delivery' described below, the Department of Transportation guarantees to purchase *80%* of the estimated quantities listed on the Bid Sheets. This minimum purchase quantity shall be the sum of the quantities in all zones awarded to each successful low bidder by NYSDOT that are serviced by a "regional distribution point." In the event a "zone" cannot accommodate the minimum purchase, fair and reasonable delivery price to other locations will be negotiated, for the quantity necessary to achieve the minimum purchase.

B) Maximum Delivery Quantity

The maximum delivery quantity required under this contract is *130%* of the estimated quantities shown on the Bid Sheets. This maximum delivery quantity is the sum of the estimated quantities in all of the zone contracts awarded to one contractor by NYSDOT.

C) Maximum Delivery Times From Placement Of Order

The maximum delivery time is *5 business days* from the time NYSDOT places the order.

D) Acceptance of "off specification" deliveries

In the event of supply difficulties experienced by the contractor, NYSDOT may accept, at its discretion, "off specification" material at a reduced price. In the ordinary supply situation, all quantity and specification requirements shall be met.

GUARANTEED EARLY DELIVERY

Most zones have a requirement for early (before December 1) delivery of material. Guaranteed Early Delivery is an attempt by the Department to reduce its costs, while at the same time helping suppliers improve the efficiency of their stockpiling and distribution operations by moving more material early in the season.

PAYMENT

Payment will be made in accordance with the unit prices indicated in the bid and subsequent Notice of Contract Award. Contractor should submit an invoice in original and three copies to the Designated Payment Office (NYSDOT Residency, unless otherwise specified).

Payments of interest on certain payments due and owed may be made in accordance with the criteria established by Chapter 153 of the Laws of 1984 (Prompt Payment) as amended.

ORDERING

Purchase orders shall be effective and binding upon the contractor when placed in the mail addressed to the contractor at the address shown on the Notice of Contract Award. Actual delivery orders shall be placed via telephone or facsimile and shall become effective immediately upon receipt by the Contractor.

The Contractor shall supply a toll-free telephone number for entering of bulk salt orders by Department Personnel. The Contractor must, upon receipt, issue a confirmation of receipt to the ordering unit.

file: salt97.026

b.   No increase in the unit price will be allowed unless the amount of increase is equal to or exceeds ten (10) cents per net ton.

c.   Any increase approved shall be retroactive to the date of the contractor's application for unit price increase unless otherwise specified by the Department. The effective date of increase shall be specified in the official notification issued by the Director of Procurement.

SPECIAL NOTE REGARDING BID RESULTS

A complete statistical tabulation of bid results will be forwarded to all bidders as soon after bids are opened as is practical - generally within 2-3 days. Please do not call the Procurement Bureau requesting bid results.

AUTHORITY OF OPERATOR

Bidders offering rock salt from a mine not owned and operated by themselves must furnish the written authority of the operator of the mine to sell rock salt from the said mine.

WEIGHT TICKETS

All shipments of bulk salt shall be accompanied by a weight ticket of a licensed weighmaster indicating the producer, net weight of the delivery, and the stockpile source. The certification must bear the weighmaster's signature; weights shall be recorded from a scale equipped with a weight printing device. Handwritten weights are not acceptable.

EFFECT OF TRANSPORTATION COST ON PRICE

Unit prices in the notice of contract award shall be subject to increases based on changes in transportation freight rates or charges, including charges for transportation by vessel, barge, rail and/or truck.

The term "Unit Price" shall be the unit price bid per net ton, F.O.B. destination, to include transportation freight rates or charges.

Bidder represents that the unit prices offered do not include any contingency allowance to cover possible increases in transportation freight rates or charges subsequent to the date of the bid opening.

Contractor(s) shall apply in writing to the Department of Transportation, Director of Procurement, for any increase in the unit price. Applications for such increases shall include as a minimum the transportation rate in effect on the date of the bid opening, the amount of such increase, the referenced published tariff or other authority promulgated by a governing regulatory body or, in the absence of such tariff or other authority, satisfactory evidence of such an increase in rates with a statement that the transportation cost requested is not more than that received from other governmental agencies or commercial concerns for like services. The State reserves the right to audit and verify the figures used to substantiate the requested increase.

Any such increases in freight rates or charges which are allowed by a governing regulatory body and are incurred by the contractors after the date of the bid opening shall correspondingly increase the contract unit price subject to the following stipulations:

a.   The aggregate of the increase shall not exceed the actual amount of the increase incurred by the contractor.

file: salt97.026

DETAILED SPECIFICATIONS

1.0 SCOPE

It is the intent of this specification to describe sodium chloride type "A" crushed rock salt, to be used for removal of ice and snow, and the requirements for construction of covered salt stockpiles by the Contractor.

1.1 CHEMICAL COMPOSITION

Shall be not less than 95% sodium chloride.   Percent of sodium chloride shall be determined in accordance with current ASTM-D-632.

1.2 SIZE GRADING

The salt, when tested, using sieves as described in ASTM-C-136 (*1) shall conform to the following requirements for particle size distribution:

Sieve Size	Per Cent Passing (*2)
1/2" - (12.5 MM)	100
3/8" - (9.5 MM)	95 - 100
No. 4 - (4.75 MM)	20 - 90
No. 8 - (2.36 MM)	10 - 60
No. 30 - (600 Microns)	0 - 15

(*1) A drying temperature of 110°C ± 5°C should be used.
(*2) Tolerance of (±) 5% on each sieve except 1/2" and 3/8" sizes, on which no tolerance   will be allowed.

file: salt97.026

1.3 MOISTURE CONTENT

Moisture content upon delivery shall not exceed 1-1/2% when determined as follows:

$$\% \text{ Moisture} = \frac{(W_1 \text{ minus } W_2)}{W_1} \times 100$$

W_1 = initial weight of sample

W_2 = weight of sample after drying to a constant weight at $100°C \pm 5°C$.

* Procedure shall be in accordance with American Water Works Association B200-88, Section 4.3. A tolerance of 0.5% will be allowed before a penalty is assessed.

1.4 ANTICAKING AGENT

Salt shall be treated with an anticaking agent. The quantity of agent used shall be in the range of 0.1 to 0.2 lbs/ton. Potential contractors shall supply with their bid a description of the agent treatment used, quantity of agent used per ton of Salt, method of determining the presence of the treatment and information relative to the solubility and photo decomposition of the treating agent. Potential harm to the ecology caused by agent treatment may be cause for rejection of a bid.

1.5 SAMPLING

Sampling shall be done in accordance with current ASTM-D632. The State or any of its authorized representatives, reserves the right to take samples from the contractor's stockpile or transfer point or from shipments at the point of destination.

The right is also reserved to consider truckloads of salt delivered by the contractor on a single day to be a single delivery. Salt picked up by DOT from a contractor's stockpile for delivery to a district stockpile on any single day may also be considered to be a single delivery. Salt so considered shall be kept separate, adequately protected from natural elements and sampled within a 24-hour period after the last truck load has been delivered. Penalties imposed because of deviation from specifications may be imposed on the total day's delivery.

1.6 DELIVERY

Rock Salt shall be shipped via bulk delivery, as specified. Trucks delivering salt to NYSDOT facilities shall have the entire cargo area completely covered by a waterproof tarpaulin or similar sheeting material. Torn or ripped coverings may be cause for rejection of the shipment. Evidence of free flowing water/brine in particular shipments may be cause for rejection.

Salt shall be received in a free-flowing and usable condition. Salt delivered in a lumpy condition which requires reprocessing in order to make it usable shall be cause for rejection of the entire delivery, with a replacement delivery to be made at no additional charge to State. If, because of emergency conditions, it is necessary to accept and reprocess the Salt for use, all reprocessing costs will be charged to the contractor.

1.7 ACCEPTANCE

The salt may be rejected if it fails to conform to any of the requirements of this specification.

1.8 PENALTIES:

1.8.1 Moisture

If, after delivery the moisture content is found to be above 2.0%, a deduction for moisture content will be made from the delivered bid price based on the following formula:

Reduced price per ton = delivered contract price per ton x (1.00 - 2X) where X=moisture content of the sample (expressed as the decimal equivalent of the percentage of the original sample weight to the nearest 1%)

1.8.2 Gradation (Particle size Distribution)

If, after delivery, the gradation of the Salt is found to be out of tolerance a deduction from the price shall be made based on the following formula:

Reduced price per ton = delivered contract price x (1.00-Y) where Y = the decimal equivalent of the total % out of gradation. The % out of tolerance for each sieve shall be to the nearest 1%. The total of the individual sieve tolerance deviations shall be used as Y.

1.8.3 General

No penalty is to be assessed unless the proper analysis and test procedures are followed.

If the contractor consistently delivers salt found to be above 2% moisture content or consistently not conforming to the gradation requirements, the contract shall be subject to cancellation either in whole or in part.

1.9 CALCULATIONS

Calculations performed relative to this specification shall be made using the rounding off method of "ASTM Recommended Practice E-29 for Designating Significant Places in Specified Limiting Values".

2.0 COVERED SALT PILES

**All outdoor covered salt piles are designated for early delivery.
As such, these piles shall be constructed and covered by December 1.**

Stockpiles will be constructed at State Facilities on State-owned pads. The ground elevation of the stockpile area shall be sufficiently above the exterior yard area to prevent inflow of storm water. The site drainage should be designed to prevent run-off from entering (seeping) under the cover and infiltrating the pile. Piles may be conical or windrow with conical ends in shape. They shall be wholly contained within the pad. Prior to installation of the covers, piles shall be neatly dressed and the salt surfaces shall generally be free of depressions, protrusions or other irregularities.

Stockpiles must be adequately protected against wind and moisture. Coverings shall be designed for a service life of six (6) months (minimum) from date of completion of the stockpile. All stockpiles must be sealed around their bases with weights or by a windrow of sand or gravel. Where wind is anticipated, covers shall be secured to anchors adequately imbedded in the ground. Covers shall also be weighted over their surface as required.

Contractor personnel shall be skilled in methods for covering salt stockpiles, including the fabrication of covers and the correct procedures to follow in covering the piles. Construction of stockpiles shall be approved by the Engineer, or his/her designee.

2.1 COVERS

Covers shall be Reinforced Plastic (Minimum weight - 6.0 oz. per sq. yd.) and shall remain workable, flexible, and show no evidence of cracking at minus twenty degrees (-20°F) Fahrenheit. The covers shall not be adversely affected by either sunlight or salt. Covers shall have a minimum tensile strength of 175 lbs. and tear strength of 60 lbs in all directions.

Other covers may be substituted subject to the approval of the Engineer at the ordering facility.

The State reserves the right to test materials at its discretion.

APPENDIX C-2
Chemical Deicer Specifications for the Pacific Northwest States of Idaho, Montana, Oregon, Washington

(provided by Washington State DOT. This document is a living document and will be updated as required.)

I.   GENERAL SPECIFICATIONS
To bid a product, vendors or manufacturers shall be on the pre-approved deicer product list, or are being qualified as part of the current bid process. The approved products list is developed by the Pacific Northwest States (PNS) of Idaho, Montana, Oregon, and Washington. The list is composed of materials that have been tested and found in conformance with these specifications. Any changes to the approved listed product by the vendor which in any way make the product different from the original qualified material will disqualify the material from the list. The product will have to be requalified before it will be allowed to be place back onto the approved list. To submit a product for the pre-approval process, contact any of the four states for information. In the case of a request for bid, please contact the state requesting the bid for information on how to become a qualified bidder.

A.   No bids will be accepted on any products that contain constituents in excess of the following established total concentration limits as tested in accordance with the listed test methodology from Section VI. Results are stated as Parts Per Million (ppm).

1.	Phosphorus	25.00 ppm
2.	Cyanide	0.20 ppm
3.	Arsenic	5.00 ppm
4.	Copper	0.20 ppm
5.	Lead	1.00 ppm
6.	Mercury	0.05 ppm
7.	Chromium	0.50 ppm
8.	Cadmium	0.20 ppm
9.	Barium	10.00 ppm
10.	Selenium	5.00 ppm
11.	Zinc	10.00 ppm

B.   No manufacturer or vendor may bid a corrosion inhibited deicer product unless qualified by successfully completing the National Association of Corrosion Engineers (NACE) Standard TM-01-69 (1976 rev.) as modified by PNS for deicer testing.
Note: The modified NACE Standard TM-01-69 (1976 rev.), requires the use of 30 milliliters of 3% solution per square inch of coupon surface for corrosion testing.

C.   The supplier of any product delivered and/or applied, that is found to be contaminated with non specified products and is cause for environmental concerns shall be responsible for all clean up expenses. This includes but is not limited to clean up measures as needed for the following: storage facility, yard, equipment, and roadside.

D.   The deicer vendor shall be liable, as determined by the purchaser for causing any unanticipated extraordinary damages to deicer equipment.

E.   Each vendor submitting a sample will be notified whether the sample passes or fails to meet specifications. Copies of the complete lab reports will be available upon request.

II.   BID PROCESS

A.   Bids must be accompanied by **two** each one gallon (4 liter) containers of the product and an analysis of the supplied samples. Analysis must contain the following information for each type of product being bid:

1.   Corrosion test data obtained according to NACE Standard TM-01-69 (1976 rev.) as modified by PNS (*providing that information is available*).

2.   pH (liquid products only)

3.   Analytical results of all constituents for which limits have been set by these specifications. (See General Specifications and the specific Category.)

4.   Specific gravity chart (liquid products only) with correlating weight and freeze point information presented in 1% increments beginning with a five percent solution. The chart must contain information up to, including, and exceeding, **by 5% (or the solubility limits of your product)** the concentration being submitted for evaluations. (See example, Exhibit A)

5.   Physical specifications including detailed information on the corrosion inhibitor used in the product and minimum concentration of the corrosion inhibitor_*MUST* be included with the bid document. Information must be sufficient in detail to address all specification requirements. Failure to provide sufficient detail to address all specification requirements may result in bid disqualification. *Proprietary information must be included and will be held confidential.*

6.   Information on the minimum corrosion control inhibitor concentration percentages and appropriate laboratory procedures for verifying concentrations must be included with the bid response. *Proprietary information must be included and will be held confidential.*

B.   Bids must be accompanied with the most recent detailed product specification sheet, and Material Safety Data Sheet (MSDS). All documents must be clearly legible.

C.   Most deicer products after successfully completing PNS's initial screening process and corrosion tests may then be required to successfully complete field application/effectiveness tests. The decision as to whether or not to require a supplier to furnish an ample supply of their product (at no charge including shipping) for field-testing lies solely with PNS. If the product requested for field-testing is not furnished, or if an inadequate amount is supplied, or if product performance is not satisfactory, the product will not be placed on the approved product list.

D.   Field application/effectiveness testing of some products may be waived based on the ingredients of the product. An example of this could be a formulation of a corrosion inhibited magnesium chloride product. PNS has laboratory and field tested many variations of this product and results of field tests should be predictable based on ingredients and percentages of those ingredients. The option to waive field application/effectiveness tests lies solely with PNS.

E.   Product samples submitted with the bid shall be sent to:

_____

_____

_____

F.   *All samples and product information must be received by the bid opening. Failure to supply the required samples and requested information in this section may be cause for disqualification of the product for testing.*
These samples will be used to establish a database for future fingerprinting of the product when delivered into any of the four states. Any products purchased in the future will be expected to meet specifications as established in the bid process. All test data that is submitted with each product sample is subject to verification by one or more of the PNS laboratories. Results of the testing from the state's laboratories shall be verifiable and final.

III.   FIELD DELIVERY OF PRODUCTS

A.   The bill of lading and/or invoice for each shipment must contain the following information.
1.   Name of product.
2.   Supplier and manufacturer of product.
3.   Destination of delivery.
4.   Contract unit of measure.
5.   Total number of units being delivered.
6.   Contract unit price for product delivered.
7.   Total weight of delivery (certified scale ticket).
8.   Total price for units delivered.
9.   Lot number of product (products) being delivered. The lot number must enable purchaser to track a delivered product back to its manufacture point, date of manufacture and specific batch.
10.   Transport information—Name of transporting company, tank, trailer or rail car number, point and date of origin.
11.   A copy of the original bill of lading.
12.   For liquid products include the Percent Concentration and Specific Gravity.

The Department will not process invoices for payment until the vendor has met all requirements under this section.

B.   Vendor will be responsible for all necessary equipment to transfer liquid deicers to purchasers' storage tanks.

C.   Purchasers storage tanks will be fitted with a 3?inch male pipe fitting to allow for unloading of product.

D.   Two one gallon (4 Liter) samples of the liquid or dry product being delivered will be taken from the delivery container.
    1.   If the load is liquid, samples will be taken from the transfer hose only after no less than one half of the load has been discharged or samples may be taken from the delivery container with a bailer tube.
    2.   If the product is dry, samples will be taken from the top 4 inches of the load prior to unloading.

E.   Each shipment shall be accompanied by a current and clearly legible MSDS.

F.   An anti-foaming agent will be available from the vendor for use as needed, at no additional charge to the State, to control foaming during loading, unloading, and agitation of liquid deicers.

G.   All orders will be placed by fax. The official order date shall be the date of the fax transmittal if received by the vendor before 2:00 p.m. (all order times reflect vendor time) and the next day if received by the vendor after 2:00 p.m.. Vendor will fax back to the buyer a confirmation of receipt and an estimate of the order shipment date within 2 business hours.

H.   All material is subject to inspection and analysis as delivered. No precipitate or flocculation in liquid products shall be allowed in excess of the specification limits. Material portraying these or other uncharacteristic traits when delivered may be immediately rejected at the option of the buyer or their representative at the delivery location.

I.   Deliveries shall be made during normal working hours (Monday through Friday between the hours of 8:00 A.M. and 4:00 P.M. for all time zones), unless otherwise requested by purchaser. Any deliveries made without proper advance notification or outside of the established delivery times (unless otherwise authorized in advance) will be assessed a minimum penalty of 25% based on the price of the product.

J.   Delivery shall be made on or within two (2) calendar days on all orders received by the vendor during the months of October to April and 15 days on orders placed during other months. In the event the vendor fails to deliver within the established number of calendar days, a deduction of 5% on the price of the product will be made per day for each day of delay beginning with day 3 or 16 (depending on month of order) and continuing until delivery is made.

There will be no deductions for the day of delivery (when late) if delivery (product is unloaded) is made before the time designated by the person placing the order. The late delivery fee assessment will be deducted from the payment of the invoice for the very load of product not delivered according to the terms of this agreement. Consistently late deliveries may result in contract termination.

K.   Any assessments or deductions charged for improper notification and/or delivery will be accompanied with verification of order and delivery date.

L.   Any penalties assessed because of late deliveries due to what the manufacture or vendor feels are "reasonable or uncontrollable circumstances" shall within seven (7) calendar days be addressed with the respective Supply Operations Supervisor. The Maintenance Engineer will make determination of whether or not assessed penalties will remain. That decision will be final.

IV.   **FIELD INSPECTION, UNLOADING, SAMPLING AND TESTING BEFORE ALLOWING ANY PRODUCT TO BE UNLOADED DEPARTMENT OF TRANSPORTATION PERSONNEL WILL ADHERE TO THE FOLLOWING PROCEDURES:**

A.   INSPECTION
   1.   Document and maintain records on all deliveries, including those that are rejected.
   2.   Check to assure that the product is being delivered according to the terms of the contract. This includes but is not limited to the following:
   a   Date of the order.
   b   Date and time of delivery.
   d   Verification of advance delivery notification.
   e   Delivered within allowable times.
   f   Name of delivery company and license plate numbers.
   g   Are any penalty assessments required?
   h   Is the product being delivered what you ordered?
   i   Document all procedures prior to unloading of product.
   j   Verify that all papers required of a delivery are present, complete, and legible.
      1.   Legible and current MSDS sheet.
      2.   Certified weight slip.
      3.   Accurate, complete, and legible bill of lading and/or invoice with the information as required in Section III Part A.

B.   SAMPLING AND TESTING

1.   A minimum of two each one-gallon (4 Liter) samples of all products will be taken from each load of product being delivered at the time of delivery. Clearly label samples for identification. Send both samples to the departments Material Testing Laboratory. One sample will be for testing and/or fingerprinting at the department's expense. The second sample will be held a minimum of 60 days in the event that the deicer does not comply with the specifications when tested. Should a delivery not meet specifications the second sample will be available for retesting *at vendor expense.* Testing results from the Headquarters Materials Laboratory will be final and in the best interest of the State.

2.   Check and record the specific gravity of the samples.

3.   Samples sent to the Headquarters Materials Laboratory will be tested for conformance to specification during the year. Each type of product may be tested for those parameters listed in the General Specifications and from the appropriate Category.

C.   UNLOADING

1.   Visually inspect the load to determine if there are any obvious reasons why the load should be rejected.

2.   Note the amount of product currently in storage prior to unloading.

3.   Visually inspect the delivered product again while unloading. If problems are noted that are a cause for rejection of the load, halt the unloading process. Take photos if applicable and record any pertinent information. Conduct the following procedures if the material is to be rejected.

a.   If material fails initial inspection or testing reload the product and reject the load.

b.   If reloading can't be done, (mixed with previous material) note the amount of product (liquid only) pumped into the tank and total product now present in the tank.

c.   Circulate the tank and then pull two one gallon (4 Liter) samples of the contaminated deicer material now in the tank

d.   Check and record the specific gravity of the samples.

e.   Take appropriate action as needed to assure the integrity of product on hand if possible. Will all products on hand have to be removed?

f.   Send samples to the Headquarters Materials Laboratory.

g.   Immediately advise the Maintenance Engineer and Purchasing of any ordering, delivery, storage, or product quality issues.

V.   DEICER CATEGORIES

Deicer Category 1
Corrosion Inhibited
Liquid Magnesium Chloride Specifications

In addition to the General Guidelines and Specifications, the following requirements also apply to liquid magnesium chloride deicer products.

1.   Product must contain no less than 25% magnesium chloride.
Test Method: Number 1

2.   Weight per gallon will be established according to the specific gravity and percentage of magnesium chloride contained in the product bid as indicated by the bidder.
Test Method: Number 2

3.   Product will contain the corrosion control inhibitor in quantities not less than those indicated by the bidder. The finished deicing product, including corrosion inhibitors, must be completely accomplished at the original manufacturing plant location. *Post adding of corrosion inhibitors or any other ingredients and splash mixing is unacceptable after the product has left the original manufacturing plant.*
Test Method: Number 3

4.   The pH must be 7.0 - 9.0
Test Method: Number 4

5.   This deicer shall not contain greater than 1.0% (V/V) Total Settleable Solids and shall have ninety-nine percent (99.0%) of the Solids Passing through a Number 10 sieve after being stored at *-17.8°C +/- 1°C (0°F +/- 2°F)* for 168 hours (Seven days).
Test Method: Number 6

Deicer Category 2
Corrosion Inhibited
Liquid Calcium Chloride Specifications

In addition to the General Guidelines and Specifications, the following requirements also apply to liquid calcium chloride deicer products.

1.   Product must contain no less than 25% calcium chloride.
Test Method: Number 1

2.   Weight per gallon will be established according to the specific gravity and percentage of calcium chloride contained in the product bid as indicated by the bidder.
Test Method: Number 2

3.   Product will contain corrosion control inhibitor in quantities not less than those indicated by the bidder. The finished deicing product, including corrosion inhibitors, must be completely accomplished at the original manufacturing plant location. *Post adding of corrosion inhibitors or any other ingredients and splash mixing is unacceptable after the product has left the original manufacturing plant.*
Test Method: Number 3

4.   The pH must be 7.0 - 9.0
Test Method: Number 4

5.   This deicer shall not contain greater than 1.0% (V/V) Total Settleable Solids and shall have ninety nine percent (99.0%) of the Solids Passing through a Number 10 sieve after being stored at *-29°C +/- 1°C (-20°F +/- 2°F)* for 168 hours (Seven days).
Test Method: Number 6

Deicer Category 3
Non Corrosion Inhibited
Liquid Calcium Magnesium Acetate
CMA Specifications (Vendor Manufactured)

In addition to the General Guidelines and Specifications, the following requirements also apply to liquid calcium magnesium acetate deicer products.

1.   Product must contain no less than 25% calcium magnesium acetate (CMA).
Test Method: Number 1

2.   Weight per gallon will be established according to the specific gravity and percentage of CMA contained in the product bid as indicated by the bidder.
Test Method: Number 2

3.   The pH must be 8.0 – 10.0
Test Method: Number 4

4.   This deicer shall not contain greater than 4.0 % (V/V) Total Settleable Solids and shall have ninety nine percent (99.0%) of the Solids Passing through a Number 10 sieve after being stored at *-12°C +/- 1°C (-10°F +/- 2°F)* for 168 hours (Seven days).
Test Method: Number 6

5.   Calcium to magnesium mole ratio shall be 0.55 to 1.00.
Test Method: Number 1

6.   Residual base shall be a maximum of 0.30 meq (milliequivalents) base per gram of sample.
Test Method: Number 11

Deicer Category 4
Corrosion Inhibited
Sodium Chloride Specifications

In addition to the General Guidelines and Specifications, the following requirements also apply to the corrosion inhibited solid sodium chloride deicer product.

1.   Gradation of product shall be Type 1, Grade 2 per ASTM D 632
     Test Method: Number 13

PHYSICAL REQUIREMENTS AND TOLERANCES

Gradation — ASTM D 632, Type I, Grade 2, Sodium Chloride			Permissible Variations, 5% allowed for each sieve size	
Sieve Size	Wt. % Passing		Wt. % Passing	Price Adjustments
3/4"	100		100	None
#4	20 - 100		15 - 100	None
#8	10 - 60		5 - 65	None
#30	0 - 15		0 - 20	None

Gradations outside the above limiting tolerances will be assessed a 25 percent price adjustment.

2.   Anti-Caking agent will be included to insure that the material remains free from hard caking and suitable for it's intended purpose.
     Test Method: Number 14

NOTE: Salt for highway use is usually treated with either Ferric Ferrocyanide, also known as Prussian Blue, or Sodium Ferrocyanide, also known as Yellow Prussiate of Soda (YPS), to prevent the salt from caking. The amount of Prussian Blue added is 70 to 165 parts per million (ppm), equivalent to 0.33 to 1.14 pounds per ton of salt. YPS is added in the amount of 50 to 250 ppm, equivalent to 0.1 to 0.5 pounds per ton of salt. YPS is also used as an anti-caking agent in table salt, and has approval of the U.S. Food and Drug Administration. Based on exhaustive testing no evidence of toxicity was demonstrated. The presence of these products will not be assessed towards the total cyanide concentration when testing this product. However, the total cyanide concentration of the original material must meet specifications. Information may be obtained from the Salt Institutes Highway Digest Publication.

3.   Material must be clean and free from extraneous matter.
     Test Method: Number 14

4.   Product must be homogenous or manufactured in such a manner to assure that the corrosion inhibitor, anti-caking agent, and the deicer can not segregate.
     Test Method: Number 14

5.   Moisture Content

The salt shall be dried to a maximum moisture content of *0.5 percent* (percent by weight). Water in excess of 0.5% of dry salt weight will not be paid for. The amount of salt to be paid for, when moisture exceeds 0.5% shall be computed as follows:

Pay Weight = 100.5 x Wet Wt. of Salt divided by lOO + % of moisture
Test Method: Number 12

6.   Corrosion Control Inhibitor and Concentration
Test Method: Number 3

Deicer Category 5
Corrosion Inhibited
Sodium Chloride Plus 10% Magnesium Chloride Specifications

In addition to the General Guidelines and Specifications, the following requirements also apply to the corrosion inhibited solid sodium chloride plus 10 percent magnesium chloride deicer product. Manufacturer must state the use of solid or liquid magnesium chloride. For liquid applications the manufacturer shall use at a minimum a 28% concentration of magnesium chloride. The manufacturer shall supply information as to what concentration of the magnesium chloride was used in the process.

1.   Gradation of product shall be Type 1, Grade 2 per ASTM D 632
Test Method: Number 13

PHYSICAL REQUIREMENTS AND TOLERANCES

Gradation — ASTM D 632, Type I, Grade 2,			Permissible Variations, 5% allowed for each sieve size	
Sieve Size	Wt. % Passing		Wt. % Passing	Price Adjustments
3/4"	100		100	None
#4	20 - 100		15 - 100	None
#8	10 - 60		5 - 65	None
#30	0 - 15		0 - 20	None

Gradations outside the above limiting tolerances will be assessed a 25 percent price adjustment.

2.   Anti-Caking agent will be included to insure that the material remains free from hard caking and suitable for it's intended purpose.
Test Method: Number 14

NOTE: Salt for highway use is usually treated with either Ferric Ferrocyanide, also known as Prussian Blue, or Sodium Ferrocyanide, also known as Yellow Prussiate of Soda (YPS), to prevent the salt from caking. The amount of Prussian Blue added is 70 to 165 parts per million (PPM), equivalent to 0.33 to 1.14 pounds per ton of salt. YPS is added in the amount of 50 to 250 PPM, equivalent to 0.1 to 0.5 pounds per ton of salt. YPS is also used as an anti-caking agent in table salt, and has approval of the U.S. Food and Drug Administration. Based on exhaustive testing no evidence of toxicity was demonstrated. The presence of these products will not be assessed towards the total cyanide concentration when testing this product. However, the total cyanide concentration of the original material must meet specifications. Information may be obtained from the Salt Institutes Highway Digest Publication.

3.   Material must be clean and free from extraneous matter.
Test Method: Number 14

4.   Product must be homogenous or manufactured in such a manner to assure that the corrosion inhibitor, anti-caking agent, and the deicer(s) can not segregate.
Test Method: Number 14

5.   Moisture Content Of Sodium Chloride Only.
     A.   Sodium Chloride Only
         The salt shall be dried to a maximum moisture content of *0.5 percent* (percent by weight). Water in excess of 0.5% of dry salt weight will not be paid for. The amount of salt to be paid for, when moisture exceeds 0.5% shall be computed as follows:
         Pay Weight = 100.5 x Wet Wt. of Salt divided by lOO + % of moisture
         Test Method: Number 12
     B.   Magnesium Chloride Hexahydrate Only
         The total moisture content of the magnesium chloride (both free and bound) shall not exceed 56%.
         *Unbound water is defined as that water that is not a normal part of the ingredients and becomes part of the product due to hygroscopic action.
         Test Method: Number 1

6.   Corrosion Control Inhibitor and Concentration
Test Method: Number 3

7.   Product Must Contain No Less Than 10% Magnesium Chloride Hexahydrate by Weight. This product will consist of 10% magnesium chloride hexahydrate ($MgCl_2 + 6H_2O$) as specified by weight. Weight of the magnesium chloride shall be calculated as a percent of the total mixture with zero percent *unbound water**. The manufacture shall establish unit densities and correlating weight for the product based on the zero percent of unbound water content at time of manufacturing. The required percentage of magnesium chloride ($MgCl_2$) in the total mixture shall be based on the weight of magnesium chloride hexahydrate ($MgCl_2 + 6H_2O$).
Test Method: Number 1

Deicer Category 6
Corrosion Inhibited
Sodium Chloride Plus 20% Magnesium Chloride Specifications

In addition to the General Guidelines and Specifications, the following requirements also apply to the corrosion inhibited solid sodium chloride plus 20 percent magnesium chloride deicer product. Manufacturer must state the use of solid or liquid magnesium chloride. For liquid applications the manufacturer shall use at a minimum a 28% concentration of magnesium chloride. The manufacturer shall supply information as to what concentration of the magnesium chloride was used in the process.

1.   Gradation of product shall be Type 1, Grade 2 per ASTM D 632
      Test Method: Number 13

PHYSICAL REQUIREMENTS AND TOLERANCES

Gradation — ASTM D 632, Type I, Grade 2,			Permissible Variations, 5% allowed for each sieve size	
Sieve Size	Wt. % Passing		Wt. % Passing	Price Adjustments
3/4"	100		100	None
#4	20 - 100		15 - 100	None
#8	10 - 60		5 - 65	None
#30	0 - 15		0 - 20	None

Gradations outside the above limiting tolerances will be assessed a 25 percent price adjustment.

2.   Anti-Caking agent will be included to insure that the material remains free from hard
      caking and suitable for it's intended purpose.
      Test Method: Number 14

NOTE: Salt for highway use is usually treated with either Ferric Ferrocyanide, also known as Prussian Blue, or Sodium Ferrocyanide, also known as Yellow Prussiate of Soda (YPS), to prevent the salt from caking. The amount of Prussian Blue added is 70 to 165 parts per million (PPM), equivalent to 0.33 to 1.14 pounds per ton of salt. YPS is added in the amount of 50 to 250 PPM, equivalent to 0.1 to 0.5 pounds per ton of salt. YPS is also used as an anti-caking agent in table salt, and has approval of the U.S. Food and Drug Administration. Based on exhaustive testing no evidence of toxicity was demonstrated. The presence of these products will not be assessed towards the total cyanide concentration when testing this product. However, the total cyanide concentration of the original material must meet specifications. Information may be obtained from the Salt Institutes Highway Digest Publication.

3.   Material must be clean and free from extraneous matter.
      Test Method: Number 14

4. Product must be homogenous or manufactured in such a manner to assure that the corrosion inhibitor, anti-caking agent, and the deicer(s) can not segregate.
    Test Method: Number 14

5. Moisture Content Of Sodium Chloride Only.
    A. Sodium Chloride Only
        The salt shall be dried to a maximum moisture content of *0.5 percent* (percent by weight). Water in excess of 0.5% of dry salt weight will not be paid for. The amount of salt to be paid for, when moisture exceeds 0.5% shall be computed as follows:
        Pay Weight = 100.5 x Wet Wt. of Salt divided by lOO + % of moisture
        Test Method: Number 12
    B. Magnesium Chloride Hexahydrate Only
        The total moisture content of the magnesium chloride (both free and bound) shall not exceed 56%.
        *Unbound water is defined as that water that is not a normal part of the ingredients and becomes part of the product due to hygroscopic action.
        Test Method: Number 1 and or 14

6. Corrosion Control Inhibitor and Concentration
    Test Method: Number 3

7. Product Must Contain No Less Than 20% Magnesium Chloride Hexahydrate by Weight. This product will consist of 20% magnesium chloride hexahydrate ($MgCl_2$ +6H2O) as specified by weight. Weight of the magnesium chloride shall be calculated as a percent of the total mixture with zero percent *unbound water**. The manufacture shall establish unit densities and correlating weight for the product based on the zero percent of unbound water content at time of manufacturing. The required percentage of magnesium chloride ($MgCl_2$) in the total mixture shall be based on the weight of magnesium chloride hexahydrate ($MgCl_2$ +6H2O).
    Test Method: Number 1

Deicer Category 7
Corrosion Inhibited Solid Calcium Magnesium Acetate Specifications

In addition to the General Guidelines and Specifications, the following requirements also apply to solid Calcium Magnesium Acetate deicer products.

1. Product will consist of Calcium Magnesium Acetate (CMA)
    Only those ingredients that are normally found in high quality CMA will be acceptable. Any products that do not meet this requirement during the bid process will be immediately rejected unless scientific data shows the additional ingredients/ingredients result in an improvement to the product.
    Test Method: Number 14

2. Calcium to magnesium mole ratio shall be 0.55 to 1.00
    Test Method: Number 1

3.   This product when liquefied at or near a 25% concentration shall not contain greater than 4.0 % (V/V) settleable solids and shall have ninety nine percent (99.0%) of the Solids Passing through a Number 10 sieve after being stored at *-12°C +/- 1°C (-10°F +/- 2°F)* for 168 hours (Seven days).
Test Method: Number 6

4.   Moisture (free and hydration) shall not exceed 10%.
Test Method: Number 12

5.   Product attrition shall be less than 2.5% with minimum dust generated on handling.
Test Method: Number 14 and any other tests deemed necessary.

6.   Residual base shall be 0.30 milliequivilent base per gram of sample.
Test Method: Number 11

7.   The pH of product in a 10% solution shall be 8 to 10.
Test Method: Number 4 except in this case a 10% solution will be used.

Deicer Category 8
Non Corrosion Inhibited
Sodium Chloride Specifications

In addition to the General Guidelines and Specifications, the following requirements also apply to the solid sodium chloride deicer product.

1.   Gradation of product shall be Type 1, Grade 2 per ASTM D 632
Test Method: Number 13

PHYSICAL REQUIREMENTS AND TOLERANCES

Gradation — ASTM D 632, Type I, Grade 2, Sodium Chloride			Permissible Variations, 5% allowed for each sieve size	
Sieve Size	Wt. % Passing		Wt. % Passing	Price Adjustments
3/4"	100		100	None
#4	20 - 100		15 - 100	None
#8	10 - 60		5 - 65	None
#30	0 - 15		0 - 20	None

Gradations outside the above limiting tolerances will be assessed a 25 percent price adjustment.

2.   Anti-Caking agent will be included to insure that the material remains free from hard caking and suitable for it's intended purpose.
Test Method: Number 14

NOTE: Salt for highway use is usually treated with either Ferric Ferrocyanide, also known as Prussian Blue, or Sodium Ferrocyanide, also known as Yellow Prussiate of Soda (YPS), to prevent the salt from caking. The amount of Prussian Blue added is 70 to 165 parts per million (PPM), equivalent to 0.33 to 1.14 pounds per ton of salt. YPS is added in the amount of 50 to 250 PPM, equivalent to 0.1 to 0.5 pounds per ton of salt. YPS is also used as an anti-caking agent in table salt, and has approval of the U.S. Food and Drug Administration. Based on exhaustive testing no evidence of toxicity was demonstrated. The presence of these products will not be assessed towards the total cyanide concentration when testing this product. However, the total cyanide concentration of the original material must meet specifications. Information may be obtained from the Salt Institutes Highway Digest Publication.

3.   Material must be clean and free from extraneous matter.
Test Method: Number 14

4.   Product must be homogenous or manufactured in such a manner to assure that the anti-caking agent, and the deicer an not segregated.
Test Method: Number 14

5.   Moisture Content
The salt shall be dried to a maximum moisture content of *0.5 percent* (percent by weight). Water in excess of 0.5% of dry salt weight will not be paid for. The amount of salt to be paid for, when moisture exceeds 0.5% shall be computed as follows:
Pay Weight = 100.5 x Wet Wt. of Salt divided by lOO + % of moisture
Test Method: Number 12

VI.   TEST METHODS

1.   **Percent Concentration of Active Ingredient In The Liquid**
Test Method: Atomic Absorption Spectrophotometry as described in "Standard Methods for the Examination of Water and Waste Water", APHA-AWWA-WPCF. Test Method 1 in the Appendix is used to determine percent concentration of Calcium Chloride or Magnesium Chloride.

2.   **Weight Per Gallon**
Test Method: Specific Gravity by ASTM D 1429 Test Method A - Pycnometer at 20° C +/- 1° C.

3.   **Corrosion Control Inhibitor Presence and Concentration**
Test Method: The Materials Laboratory may use the test procedures provided by the bidder or manufacture for testing quantitative concentrations of additives. These same tests can then be used to verify that materials being delivered are the same as those previously tested and approved in the bid process.

4. **pH**
    Test Method: ASTM E 70 except a dilution shall be made of 1 part deicer to 4 parts distilled water before attempting a reading.

5. **Corrosion Rate**
    Test Method: NACE Standard TM-01-69 (1976 revision) as modified by PNS. This procedure is listed as Test Method 2 in Appendix A of Appendix C-2.

6. **Percent Total Settleable Solids and Percent Solids Passing a 10 Sieve**
    Test Method: This procedure is listed as Test Method 3 in Appendix A of Appendix C-2.

7. **Total Phosphorus**
    Test Method: Total Phosphorous as described in "Standard Methods for the examination of Water and Waste Water", APHA-AWWA-WPCF. Total phosphorus shall be determined upon a 1% test solution. The Total Phosphorus value determined from the 1% solution is the value to be reported without being calculated for the dilution. The test solution should be prepared by placing 10 ml of sample into 500 ml of ASTM D 1193 Type II distilled water contained in a 1 L volumetric flask to which 2.5 ml 1 + 1 sulfuric acid has been added. Swirl the contents and make up to 1000 ml with distilled water.

8. **Total Cyanide**
    Test Method: Total Cyanide as described in "Standard Methods for the examination of Water and Waste Water", APHA-AWWA-WPCF.

9. **Total Arsenic, Barium, Cadmium, Chromium, Copper, Lead, Selenium and Zinc.**
    Test Method: Atomic Absorption Spectrophotometry as described in "Standard Methods for the examination of Water and Waste Water", APHA-AWWA-WPCF.

10. **Total Mercury**
    Test Method: Cold Vapor Atomic Absorption Spectrophotometry as described in "Standard Methods for the examination of Water and Waste Water", APHA-AWWA-WPCF.

11. **Milliequivalents OR "meq"**
    Test Method: This is a measure of the amount of unreacted base in the product. "meq" means milliequivalents or the milligrams of acetic acid to neutralize 1 gram of unreacted base.
    Method for measuring unreacted base is a standard acid/base titration procedure. A fixed volume of acid (30 ml of 0.1 N HCl) is added to 1 gram sample of CMA. The excess acid is titrated with a standard base (0.1 N NaOH) to phenopthalein endpoint, pH of 8.6.

12. **Moisture Content Of Solid Deicer Products.**
    Test Method: According to ASTM   E 534

13.   **Gradation**
Test Method: According to ASTM D 632

14.   **Visual Inspection and Field Observations.**
Test Method: Visual inspection and field observations to assure that the material remains clean and free of extraneous matter, free from hard caking, does not segregate, and remains suitable for the intended purpose and as otherwise outlined in Section IV.
NOTE: Purchaser may use any laboratory test method necessary to verify conclusions from visual inspections.

VII.   PENALTIES FOR DEVIATIONS FROM SPECIFICATIONS

Penalty/penalties will be assessed on product cost, excluding freight. Determination of a penalty to be applied will be based on the PNS testing procedures as outlined in the specifications. Penalty maximums shall not exceed 75% of material cost only.

VIII.   PENALTY BASED ON MAGNESIUM OR CALCIUM CHLORIDE CONCENTRATION

Field samples taken of the delivered liquid deicer will be tested for Magnesium Chloride, Calcium Chloride, and Calcium Magnesium Acetate concentration in percent according to Test Method 1. The test results will be compared to the vendor quoted concentration (VQC) of deicer. Since this contract is awarded based on the lowest price per percent concentration of deicer for each Category, a penalty structure is constructed to insure that the vendor quoted concentrations (VQC) are maintained. The percent values indicated below are percent concentration of magnesium or calcium chloride not percentage of the VQC.   If the test results are out of specification, the supplier will be subject to a penalty based on the total weight of the respective shipment as follows:
(At no time are any of the applied percentages allowed to reduce the concentration below the minimum concentration limit.)

VARIANCE FROM SPECIFICATION PENALTIES

Penalties for noncompliance of material to the Vendor Quoted Concentration (VQC)

Concentration Ranges

VQC less 1.0% but in no case below the minimum concentration limit — No penalty
VQC less 1.1% and above but in no case below the minimum concentration limit — 35% Penalty

Penalties for deicer below the minimum concentration are as follows:

Category I Penalties

24.0% to 24.9% —   50% Penalty
23.9% and below —   75% Penalty

Category II Penalties

24.0% to 24.9% — 50% Penalty
28.9% and below — 75% Penalty

IX.   GENERAL PENALTIES

Products, which fail to meet any of the other specification requirements (outside of acceptable range), will result in a 50% penalty assessment or total rejection as per the purchasers discretion. The supplier will be required to replace any rejected material plus any material that it contaminated at their cost. Any product that is rejected shall be removed by the supplier and replaced with product that meets the material specifications, including handling and transportation charges at no additional cost to the purchaser. Removal includes the removal of all material contaminated by the non-specification material if any. Purchaser's personnel will establish the amount of material contaminated.

Two shipments per contract year of product found by purchaser to be beyond any acceptable range may result in contract termination.

X.   BID SCHEDULE

A.   BEST BUY DETERMINATION *(Approved Liquid Deicers)*
Best buy (FOB delivery destination) based on percentage of deicer in the product will be determined by the following formula. **Vendor quoted concentrations and price per ton will be used for calculations.** Delivered Price/concentration % (as a whole number) equals the best buy. (The vendor quoted concentration will be in the calculation.) Example:
a. $60.00/25   = $2.40 per unit of deicer chemical.
b. $65.00/30   = $2.16 per unit of deicer chemical.
Example "b" at the higher cost per ton but with the higher concentration would be determined to be the best buy.
Acceptance of bids will be based on approved laboratory results and the lowest cost per percentage (%) of concentration of liquid deicer for bulk or barrel delivery. Bids will be awarded on these parameters to each individual District location.

B.   PRODUCT INFORMATION AND VENDOR QUOTED CONCENTRATION

Vendor's response to the following items will be considered representative of their product. During testing of the bid samples, submitted samples cannot deviate from the percent concentration by more than plus or minus one full percentage of the vendor quoted concentration as indicated below. If the bid samples exceed this deviation tolerance, that bid will be disqualified. It is to the vendor's advantage to have the submitted sample match as exactly as possible the quoted concentration. At no time will any sample be allowed to be below the minimum concentration requirement for that product as stated in these specifications. Failure to supply any part of this information is cause for rejection.

1.   The product being bid is sold under the brand name of

_____

2.   The product is manufactured by

_____

3.   The product has a concentration of _____ %. **

This is the Vendor Quoted Concentration <u>NO</u> ranges please. If a range is used, the lowest vendor specified concentration will be used for cost analysis.

C.   PRICE

The following quantities of deicers are projected from use records from the past seasons. These quantities are to be used for bidding purposes only. They are not guaranteed deliverable quantities as the winter weather can and does change and quantities may be less or more than what is being represented. **All prices are to be bid per ton and based on BULK DELIVERY, FOB point of delivery.**

D.   Product, Delivery Locations & Quantities

1.   Location: _____

Product name:

_____

Estimated Quantity:

_____

Delivery Information:

_____

_____

	Number of units in full load.	Total at FOB Locations
Liquid Deicer		
Bulk Delivery (truck tanker)	_____	_____
Bulk Delivery (Rail Tanker)	_____	_____
55 gallon barrel	_____	_____
	_____	_____
Solid Deicer		
Bulk Delivery (truck)	_____	_____
Bulk Delivery (Rail)	_____	_____
Super Sacks, (weight)	_____	_____
Bags, (weight)	_____	_____

2.   Location:

_____

Product name:

_____

Estimated Quantity

_____

Delivery Information:

_____

_____

	Number of units in full load.	Total at FOB Locations
Liquid Deicer		
Bulk Delivery (truck tanker)	_____	_____
Bulk Delivery (Rail Tanker)	_____	_____
55 gallon barrel	_____	_____
Solid Deicer		
Bulk Delivery (truck)	_____	_____
Bulk Delivery (Rail)	_____	_____
Super Sacks, (weight)	_____	_____
Bags, (weight)	_____	_____

EXHIBIT A

FREEZING POINT OF MAGNESIUM CHLORIDE BRINE

EXAMPLE OF A 25% PRODUCT SUBMITTED

% by weight	Specific Gravity	Freezing point Celsius	Freezing point Fahrenheit
5	1.013	-2.11	26.4
6	1.051	-3.09	25.0
7	1.060	-4.72	23.5
8	1.069	-5.67	21.8
9	1.070	-6.67	20.0
10	1.086	-7.83	17.9
11	1.096	-9.05	15.7
12	1.105	-10.5	13.1
13	1.114	-12.1	10.3
14	1.123	-13.7	7.3
15	1.132	-15.9	4.0
16	1.142	-17.6	0.4
17	1.151	-19.7	-3.5
18	1.161	-22.1	-7.7
19	1.170	-25.6	-12.2
20	1.180	-27.4	-17.2
21	1.190	-30.5	-23.0
22	1.200	-32.8	-27.0
23	1.210	-28.9	-20.0
24	1.220	-25.6	-14.0
**25	**1.230	**-23.3	**-10.0
26	1.241	-21.1	-6.0
27	1.251	-19.4	-3.0
28	1.262	-18.3	-1.0
29	1.273	-17.2	1.0
30	1.283	-16.7	3.0

**25% EXAMPLE. YOUR INFORMATION MUST MATCH YOUR PRODUCT. **

APPENDIX A of APPENDIX C-2
Test Procedures Adopted by the Pacific Northwest States for Deicer Testing

INDEX

TEST METHOD 1 – Concentration Percentage of Active Ingredient In Liquid Deicer

TEST METHOD 2 – Corrosion Rate As Conducted From The NACE Standard TM-01-69 (1976 Revision) As Modified By The Pacific Northwest States

TEST METHOD 3 – Percent Total Settleable Solids And Percent Solids Passing A No. 10 Sieve

TEST METHOD 1
Concentration Percentage of Active Ingredient In Liquid Deicer

I.   **Test Method**

Atomic Absorption Spectrophotometry as described in "Standard Methods for the Examination of Water and Waste Water", APHA-AWWA-WPCF

II.   **Apparatus**

Atomic Absorption Spectrophotometer
250, 500 ml Graduated Cylinders
2000 ml Beaker
100, 500, 1000 ml Volumetric Flasks
5, 10, 15, 20, 25, 30 ml Volumetric Pipets
100 microliter Eppendorf Pipet

III.   **Reagents**

ASTM D 1193 Type II Distilled Water
1000 ppm Calcium Solution made from an Analyzed Reagent Grade Chemical or a
        purchased Certified Stock Solution
1000 ppm Magnesium Solution made from an Analyzed Reagent Grade Chemical or a
        purchased Certified Stock Solution
Concentrated Hydrochloric Acid (Hcl)
Concentrated Nitric Acid (HNO_3)
Lanthanum Oxide (La_2O_3), Reagent Grade

IV.   **Preparation of Lanthanum Chloride, Calcium Chloride, Magnesium Chloride, Blank, and Quality Control Solutions**

1.   Preparation of Lanthanum Chloride

10% Lanthanum stock solution
In a 2000 ml beaker add 200 ml of distilled water to 117.28 g of Lanthanum Oxide. While stirring, **very slowly** add 500 ml of concentrated HCl (25 ml at a time). ***CAUTION!*** This reaction is extremely violent. Care should be taken so solution does not overflow the beaker. When the solution has cooled to room temperature, transfer to a 1000 ml volumetric flask and dilute to volume with distilled water. (Lanthanum Chloride is the Ionization Suppressant used in determining Calcium and Magnesium concentrations by Atomic Absorption).

2.   Calcium and Magnesium Chloride Solutions

Calcium
A.   *100 ppm Calcium Stock Solution for Dilutions* Using a volumetric pipet, measure 10 ml of the 1000 ppm Calcium reagent solution into a 100 ml volumetric flask. Using an eppendorf pipet add 0.1 ml concentrated HNO3 acid and dilute to volume with distilled water.
B.   *Calcium Standards for Calibration (20, 25, 30 ppm)* Using volumetric pipets measure 20, 25, and 30 ml of the above 100 ppm Calcium stock solution into three different 100 ml volumetric flasks. Add 20 ml of the 10% Lanthanum Chloride solution to each flask and dilute to volume with distilled water.

Magnesium
A.   *100 ppm Magnesium Stock Solution for Dilutions* Using a volumetric pipet, measure 10 ml of the 1000 ppm Magnesium reagent solution into a 100 ml volumetric flask. Using an eppendorf pipet add 0.1 ml concentrated HNO_3 acid and dilute to volume with distilled water.
B.   *Magnesium Standards for Calibration (10, 15, 20 ppm)* Using volumetric pipets measure 10, 15, and 20 ml of the above 100 ppm Magnesium solution into three different 100 ml volumetric flasks. Add 20 ml of the 10% Lanthanum Chloride solution to each flask and dilute to volume with distilled water.

3.   Blank Solution
A.   *Blank Solution for Calibration* Pipette 20 ml of 10% Lanthanum Chloride solution into a 100 ml volumetric flask and dilute to volume with distilled water.

4.   Quality Control Solutions
A.   <u>Calcium Quality Control Check</u> Weigh 0.6762 g pre-dried $CaCO_3$ and place into a 1000ml volumetric flask. Add 1 ml concentrated HNO_3 and dilute to volume with distilled water. From this solution, pipette 10 ml into a 100 ml volumetric flask, add 20 ml of the 10% Lanthanum Chloride solution and bring to volume with distilled water. This will be the working Quality Control Standard and have a value of **27.1 ppm Calcium**. (Note: The 27.1 ppm Calcium concentration is equal to a 30% brine concentration of Calcium Chloride based on a 2.5 gram sample size.)
B.   *Magnesium Chloride Quality Control Check* Weigh 1.3341 g (nondried) $MgCl_2$-$6H_2O$ and place into 1000 ml volumetric flask. Add 1 ml concentrated HNO_3 and dilute to volume with distilled water. From this solution, pipette 10 ml into a 100 ml volumetric flask, add 20 ml of the 10% Lanthanum Chloride solution and bring to volume with distilled water. This will be the working Quality Control Standard and have a value of **16.0 ppm Magnesium.** Note: (Note: The 16.0 ppm Magnesium concentration is equal to a 25% brine concentration of Magnesium Chloride based on a 2.5 gram sample size.)

V.   Preparation of Deicer Sample Solution

Solution A
1.   Weigh approximately 2.500 grams of the liquid deicer into a tared 500 ml volumetric flask. Record the sample weight to the nearest mg for final calculations. Add l ml HNO_3. Dilute to volume with distilled water. Label as solution A.

Solution B (Working Deicer Solution)
2.   Pipette 5 ml of Solution A into a 100 ml volumetric flask. Add 20 ml of 10% Lanthanum Chloride solution and dilute to volume with distilled water. Label as solution B (Dilution factor of 20).
3.   Repeat Step 2 so that each deicer sample has a duplicate working solution.

VI.   Atomic Absorption Spectrophotometer Operation

Calcium
1.   Set up the spectrophotometer (absorption) with the Calcium lamp using a wavelength setting of 422.4 nm, and a slit width of 0.2 nm. An Air-Acetylene flame should be used with the 10 cm burner head set at a 45^0 angle. The flame, burner, and instrument are to be optimized for best detection.
2.   Calibrate the instrument using the blank, 20 ppm, 25 ppm, and 30 ppm standards for Calcium.
3.   Run the Calcium Quality Control solution. This result must be within plus or minus 0.2 ppm of the known 27.1 ppm concentration before proceeding.
4.   Once the Quality Control solution is within allowable limits, run the deicer samples and their duplicates and record the results.
5.   Run the Calcium Quality Control solution again to assure accurate results.
6.   Following the analysis calculate the percent concentration of the sample and the duplicate sample for each deicer using the following formulas. These test results must be repeatable within plus or minus 0.3% concentration of each other to be acceptable for reporting.   If the results are outside this allowable limit, perform the dilutions over and retest until the samples are repeatable within the 0.3% limit.

Magnesium
1.   Set up the spectrophotometer (absorption) with the Magnesium lamp using a wavelength setting of 285.4 nm, and a slit width of 0.2 nm. An Air Acetylene flame should be used with the 10 cm burner head set at a 45^0 The flame, burner, and instrument are to be optimized for best detection.
2.   Calibrate the instrument using the blank, 20 ppm, 25 ppm, and 30 ppm standards for Magnesium.
3.   Run the Magnesium Quality Control solution. This result must be within plus or minus 0.15 ppm of the known 16.0 ppm concentration before proceeding.
4.   Once the Quality Control solution is within allowable limits, run the deicer samples and their duplicates and record the results.

5. Run the Magnesium Quality Control solution again to assure accurate results.
6. Following the analysis calculate the percent concentration of the sample and the duplicate sample for each deicer using the following formulas. These test results must be repeatable within plus or minus 0.3% concentration of each other to be acceptable for reporting. If the results are outside this allowable limit, perform the dilution's over and retest until the samples are repeatable within the 0.3% limit.

VII.   Calculations

Calculations for $CaCl_2$ base on a sample weighing 2.550 grams :

$$Factor = \frac{(110.99\ CaCl_2)(1\%)(Dilution\ factor)(Initial\ vol.)\ \overset{(20)}{}\ \overset{(500\ ml)}{}}{} = 2.7691$$

$$\%\ CaCl_2 = \frac{(X\ ppm\ from\ AA\ Anal.)(Factor)\ \overset{(40.08\ Ca)}{}\ \overset{(10,000\ ppm)}{}}{grams\ of\ sample}$$

Example: $\dfrac{(38.50\ PPM)(2.7692)}{2.5500\ g\ deicer} = 41.81\%\ CaCl_2$

Calculations for $MgCl_2$ base on a sample weighing 2.550 grams :

$$Factor = \frac{(95.211\ MgCl_2)(1\%)(Dilution\ factor)(Initial\ vol.)\ \overset{(20)}{}\ \overset{(500\ ml)}{}}{(24.305\ Mg)\ \underset{(10,000\ ppm)}{}} = 3.91734$$

$$\%\ MgCl_2 = \frac{(X\ ppm\ from\ AA\ Anal.)(Factor)}{grams\ of\ sample}$$

Example: $\dfrac{(18.87\ ppm)(3.91734)}{2.5500\ g\ deicer} = 29.57\%\ MgCl_2$

TEST METHOD 2
Corrosion Rate As Conducted From The NACE Standard TM-01-69 (1976 Revision) And As Modified By The Pacific Northwest States

When these requirements are met the product is then subjected to the corrosion test. Based on PNS laboratory corrosion tests (National Association of Corrosion Engineers (NACE) Standard TM-01-69 (1976 rev.), PNS modified), the corrosion inhibited deicer product must prove to have a corrosion value of at least 70% less than Sodium Chloride (salt) to be acceptable. **PNS has modified this procedure so that the test procedure uses 30 ml of a 3% deicer solution per square inch of coupon surface area for the corrosion test.**

I.   PREPARATION OF THE COUPONS

The coupons used are 1/2" (approximately 1.38 in. x 0.56 in. x 0.11 in.) flat steel washers displaying a density of approximately 7.85 grams per cubic centimeter. (Note: No galvanized coupons are allowed to be used even after removing the zinc with acid. Hot dipped galvanization creates a Fe-Zn metallurgical surface bond that changes the characteristics of the steel. Coupons must meet ASTM F 436, Type 1, with a Rockwell Hardness of C 38-45. Each coupons used in the test procedure is subjected to the following process to assure accuracy in test results.

* Wipe with suitable solvent to remove grease and oil.

* Examine each coupon for metallurgical abnormalities and reject those that are suspect to flaws.

* All coupons are tested for Rockwell Hardness of C 38-45; coupons having hardness outside of this range are rejected.

* Acceptable coupons are stamped for identification.

* Coupons are acid etched with 1 + 1 HCl for approximately 2 -3 minutes.

* The coupons are then quickly rinsed with tap water, distilled water, wiped dried and placed in chloroform.

* When the coupons are removed from the chloroform for use, they are place on a paper-lined tray (not touching each other) and allowed to air dry in a ventilated hood for a minimum of 15 minutes.

* Coupons are measured as specified. (Note: If latex gloves are not worn during measuring, the coupons should be rinsed again and dried as prescribe above prior to weighing. This will remove any oils that may be transferred to the coupons.)

* Each coupon shall be weighed to a constant weight. The constant weight shall be two consecutive weighings of each coupon within a minimum of 0.5 milligrams of each other. Removal of incidental flash rusting prior to weighing is not necessary.

Three coupons are used in each deicer solution and for the distilled water and Sodium Chloride control standards.

II.   MEASURING OF THE COUPONS

The outside diameter, inside diameter, and the thickness of each coupon is measured twice at 90 degrees from each initial reading and the averages calculated for each measurement. The averages are then used to calculate the surface area of each coupon with the following formula:

$$A = (3.1416/2)(D^2 - d^2) + 3.1416(t)(D) + 3.1416(t)(d)$$

Where D =   average outside diameter
               d =   average inside diameter
               t =   average thickness

Example:
$A = (1.5708)(1.9044-0.3136) + 0.4768949 + 0.1935226$
$A = (1.5708)(1.5908) + 0.4768949 + 0.1935226$
$A = 2.4988286 + 0.4768949 + 0.1935226$
$A = 3.1692461$ square inches (Total surface area of the coupon.)
$A = 3.17$ square inches

III.   PREPARATION OF THE SOLUTIONS

ASTM D 1193 Type II distilled water is used to prepare each solution, blank, and control standard. The Sodium Chloride (NaCl) used to prepare the salt standard shall be of "ANALYZED REAGENT GRADE" quality.

A 3% solution of NaCl is prepared by weight, using the reagent grade salt and distilled water.

A **3%** solution of each deicer to be tested is prepared using distilled water to dissolve and or dilute the deicer. For liquid deicer products, three parts liquid deicer product (as received) is mixed with 97 parts distilled water to produce the test solution. If the deicer product is a dry product, then the 3% solution is made by weight.

All solutions including the distilled water blank are covered an allowed to sit a minimum of 12 hours to stabilize and reach equilibrium, ensure solubility and to account for any reactivity that may occur.

IV.   THE CORROSION TEST

Approximately 300 milliliters (actual volume is determined by the surface area of test coupons) of each solution as mixed with distilled water and is put into a 500 milliliter erlynmeyer flask. Each flask is equipped with a rubber stopper that has been drilled to allow a line to run through it. One end of the line is attached to a rotating bar and the other end of the line is attached to a plastic frame made to hold coupons inside the flask where *three coupons* are attached to each plastic frame. The rotating bar is controlled by an electric timer that lowers the bar for 10 minutes then raises the bar for 50 minutes out of the solution but still keeps the coupons inside of the flask for the entire duration of the test. This allows the coupons to be exposed to the test solution 10 minutes of each hour. The corrosion test is then run for 72 hours. No agitation of the solution is made during the corrosion test.

Corrosion tests are conducted at normal room temperature. The room temperature is to be recorded daily during the operation of the test. The room temperature shall be taken with a calibrated thermometer located next to the corrosion-testing instrument. The temperature readings will be used to help determine varying corrosion rates, at this time the readings will not be used to correct data.

V. CLEANING OF THE COUPONS

The coupons are removed from the solution after 72 hours. They are placed into glass beakers containing the cleaning acid, concentrated hydrochloric acid (HCL) containing 50 grams/liter $SnCl_2$ (stannous chloride) and 20 grams/liter $SbCl_3$ (antimony trichloride). The two salts are added to the HCL to stop the reaction of the HCL with the steel once the rust or corrosion is removed. (Note: The fumes given off by the acid during cleaning contain gases formed from the antimony and are extremely hazardous, this portion of the cleaning must be conducted under a ventilated hood.)

After 15 minutes of cleaning the coupons are removed from the cleaning acid, rinsed with tap water and then distilled water, and wiped with a cloth to clean any deposit from the coupons. They are then returned to the cleaning acid and the procedure is repeated. After cleaning the coupons are rinsed in chloroform, air dried, and weighed.

Each coupon shall be weighed to a constant weight. The constant weight shall be two consecutive weighings of each coupon within a minimum of 0.5 milligrams of each other.

VI. EVALUATION OF CORROSION

The weight loss of each coupon is determined by subtracting the final weight from the original weight. The corrosion rate for each coupon is expressed as mils penetration per year (MPY) by the following formula:

MPY = (weight loss (milligrams)) (534) / ((area) (time) (metal density))

OR

MPY = (weight loss (milligrams)) (534) divided by ((area) (time) (metal density)*)
(Density is 7.85 g/cc for steel*)

The final MPY value for each solution is determined by calculating an average of the three individual coupons. *Average MPY from this point forward will be referred to as only MPY of the solution being tested.* (Note: Wide variation of MPY of individual coupons inside the same flask typically indicates contamination of a coupon. If variation of individual MPY is too great to determine consistent data the test should be run over again. Typically coupon variation may run plus or minus 3 MPY.)

VII. EXPLANATION

To put the information into perspective it is necessary to briefly recap the corrosion test process. The corrosion value of the distilled water and the reagent grade sodium chloride is critical to this whole process. These are the two base lines used to determine a products acceptability in terms of corrosion value only.

In the table following the distilled water proved to have a corrosion value of 6.00 MPY. The chart shows that the reagent grade sodium chloride has a corrected corrosion value of 45.00 MPY. This means that the original corrosion value of the reagent grade sodium chloride and the distilled water (in a 3% solution) was 51.00 MPY. That is, 6.00 MPY for the distilled water and 45.00 MPY for the reagent grade sodium chloride. The 6.00 MPY value for the distilled water was subtracted from the original 51.00 MPY for the reagent grade sodium chloride and distilled water solution to arrive at the distilled water corrected value of 45.00 MPY for the reagent grade sodium chloride.

The corrosion value of 6.00 MPY for the distilled water is subtracted from the total MPY for each of the 3% solutions for each product tested. When this calculation is completed for each product being tested the resulting value indicates the corrected corrosion value.

According to criteria adopted by PNS; "Only corrosion inhibited deicers that are at least 70% less corrosive than reagent grade sodium chloride may be used". To determine if a product is acceptable, take the corrected corrosion value of the reagent grade sodium chloride and multiply it by 30%. In this case, 45.00 MPY multiplied by 30% equals 13.5 MPY which is the highest acceptable corrected corrosion value for any product in this test. Any product in this test, that produces a MPY value higher than 13.5 MPY is rejected.

VIII.   NEGATIVE NUMBERS

Some products actually end up with a negative number as their corrected MPY value. A negative number is exceptionally good and it actually indicates that the product when mixed with distilled water in a 3% solution is less corrosive than distilled water.

To show an example of a negative number note that in Table 1 the distilled water in this test had a corrosion factor of 6.00 MPY. Also, note that the 3% solution of Wondermelt-A had a corrected corrosion value of -5.18 MPY. To quickly repeat the math used to arrive at this negative number the 3% solution corrosion value of 1.18 MPY, had subtract from it the distilled water corrosion value of 6.00 MPY. This resulted in the corrected MPY value of -5.18. The larger the negative number, the better a product is in terms of corrosion inhibiting abilities.

IX.   REPORTING RESULTS

Results shall be reported in Percent Effectiveness. Percent values less than or equal to 30% are passing. The distilled water corrected values of the deicer and the salt are used to make this calculation. The corrected value of the deicer is divided by the corrected value of the salt, this value is then multiplied by 100 to give percent.

Example: Magic Melter II has a corrected value of 10.15
               Salt has a corrected value of 45.00
Therefore: (10.15 / 45.00) X 100 = 22.6% Pass

               Acme Melter has a corrected value of 19.99
Therefore: (19.99 / 45.00) X 100 = 44.4% Fail

TABLE 1
DEICER PRODUCTS CORROSION TEST RESULTS
ALL VALUES ARE DISTILLED WATER CORRECTED

PRODUCT	MILS/YEAR	PERCENTAGE	REMARKS
*Super Stuff	-0.03	-0.07	Good stuff.
*Ice Melter	0.035	0.08	Good
*Magic Melter	1.00	2.22	Smells good
*Magic Melter II	10.15	22.55	OK
Acme Melter	19.99	44.42	Nice appearance
Acme Melter-1	23.71	52.69	50% @#*&^
Wondermelt	54.07	120.16	Very corrosive
*Wondermelt -A	-5.18	-11.51	Good corrosion protection
Stuff	17.00	37.78	not so good
SALT	**45.00**	**100.00**	
Distilled Water	**6.00**	**13.33**	

* ACCEPTABLE PRODUCT

NOTE: The results used in the above table are for example only, and they are not firm numbers. The MPY corrosion values of the distilled water and the reagent grade sodium chloride may vary from test to test.

TEST METHOD 3
Percent Total Settleable Solids and Percent Solids Passing a No.10 Sieve

This test method is used to determine the amount of total settleable solids and the percent solids passing the 10 sieve that are generated from a liquid deicer product when stored at a cold temperature without agitation.

Settleable Solids for this procedure are typically formed from chemical precipitation or crystallization, solidification, or by the settlement of any other components of the deicing product. Chemical precipitates and crystals can form when a solution is cooled below its saturation point. Solidification is the physical characteristic by which ice crystals intermixed with deicing product. Solidification can range from a few ice crystals being generated to the complete sample being converting to slush. The settlement of any additional component(s) of the product exhibits that product?s lack of ability to maintain a complete suspension without agitation. Total settleable solids will consist of all three parameters being considered together and will be reported as one value.

Percent Solids Passing the 10 Sieve will be measured by subtracting the volume retained on the sieve from the total sample volume.

I.   **Apparatus**

>   1-Liter graduated imhoff cone
>   ASTM E 11 No. 10 sieve
>   Rubber policeman
>   Graduated cylinder
>   Watch glass

II.   **Test Method**

>   Place 1000 ml of a well-mixed (non-diluted) deicer sample into a graduated one-Liter imhoff cone. Place this sample into a freezer, which has been precalibrated and stabalized to the correct temperature as established in each liquid deicer category. Cover the sample with a watch glass. The sample shall remain in the freezer *unagitated* for a period of 168 hours. Record the temperature of the freezer daily to assure proper testing temperature. After 168 hours the sample is carefully removed from the freezer for testing.

>   1.   Total Settleable Solids

>   Measure and record the volume of settleable solids using the calibrated gradations on the cone. The total settleable solids are reported in percent based upon the volume to volume (V/V) ratio of the settleable solids to the initial sample size. (Note: If the settled matter contains pockets of liquid between large settled particles, estimate the volume of these and subtract them from the volume of settled solids.)

2.   Percent Solids Passing the 10 Sieve

Immediately after determining the total settleable solids inverted the cone (or remove the tip on some models) and pour the sample through an ASTM E 11 certified Number 10 sieve. The sample should be poured through one-quarter section of the sieve if possible to reduce the surface area from which the sample must be retrieved. The sample on the sieve is not rinsed or pushed through the sieve by any means. All material not flowing through the sieve is rubber policed from the sieve into a graduated cylinder and the volume measured. Rubber police only the side the material was place on to pass through the sieve. Material that is trapped in the mesh of the sieve and does not come loose on the face of the sieve is considered passing and is not included. This volume is subtracted from the total volume of the sample to calculate the sample volume passing. The solids passing the No. 10 sieve are reported in percent based upon the volume to volume (V/V) ratio of sample volume passing to the initial sample size.

APPENDIX C-3
1000 Gallon, Slip In Skid Mounted, Liquid Deicer Application System.

This specification was provided by the Washington State Department of Transportation (WSDOT).

The document was provided via electronic media. Alterations have been made to produce a format consistent with the Guide format. Contact WSDOT for the latest version.

The intent of this specification is to describe a skid mounted sprayer assembly that will perform liquid de-ice applications. The sprayer will have an automated sprayer control system that will maintain desired application rates per lane mile when ground speed or boom width is changed. The control console must have radar speed sensor for monitoring ground speed. It will be fitted with components that are compatible with corrosive liquids. Skid assembly will have automotive enamel finish standard. All components to be new, current standard production models and will be prepared and serviced for customer use. System will be supplied with installation and training for basic operation and maintenance.

I.   TANK AND MOUNTING ASSEMBLY

A.   TANK - The main liquid storage tank to be an oval shape with a capacity of 1000 gallons. Tank is to have a maximum 5″ wide flat area, full length of tank that included 6″ sump providing total drainage of tank. Tank must not have recesses/legs for accumulation of insoluable material. Tank will be equipped with a full-length venturi jet agitation system for complete agitation of material. Tank to include a 16″ manway and 4″ center lid that is secured with a poly rope attached to the pump inlet siphon hose located in the tank sump. The tank will be constructed of linear polyethylene FDA approved resin and will be yellow in color. Tank to have specific gravity of 1.3. The tank must be compatible with all de-ice materials currently available. Tank to have diameters of 49″ tall x 78″ wide x 90″ long and carry a minimum 3-year manufacturer's warranty. Leg tanks of any type are unacceptable.

B.   MOUNTING ASSEMBLY - The main frame must be constructed to provide continuous duty support, made of steel 2″ square tubing, 3/16″ thickness, and will have a foot print of 53-1/2″ wide and 119″ long. Maximum overall length of 120″ when de-ice boom removed. Tank shall have full-length 2″ tubing supports above for added strength and have minimum 1″ bar eye hooks that will allow lifting of empty applicator. Tank must be held in place with three steel bands. The skid assembly fastens into a 5-yard dump truck bed, using the tailgate pinholes at rear and chain binders on the front. All necessary brackets and plates for mounting the pumping and flow control system will be included.

C.   CARRIER TANK AGITATION - System must contain an agitation system. It shall consist of full-length, bottom mounted venturi agitation (minimum of 10 outlets), supplied from the carrier pump. Agitation will not allow solids contained in some products to settle in the tank. Venturi agitators must be made of chemical resistant polypropylene material. The full-length venturi jet agitation must allow for a minimum of 80 GPM (Gallons Per Minute) inlet flow rate with a circulation rate of 400 GPM. A manual poly control valve will be installed in a convenient, reachable from the ground location to regulate main pump return flow to venturi jet agitation system.

II.   PUMPING SYSTEM

A.   PUMP - The main product pump to be a hydraulic driven centrifugal   pump (Hypro 9304C-HM or equal) capable of up to 190 GPM flow rate with a maximum pressure of 130 PSI. Inlet size of 2" NPT and outlet size of 1-1/2" NPT. Hydraulic motor capacity will be matched to existing hydraulic system. The pumping system must achieve 40 PSI (Pounds Per Square Inch) spray pressure at an operating volume of 3 lanes wide, at 75 gallons per mile, at 30 MPH (Miles Per Hour).

B.   PRIMING PUMP - Pump to also have 12-volt DC diaphragm style priming pump installed on face plate to assure positive priming of main pump when control console is powered. This feature will evacuate air from pump supply lines protecting main pump seal, and allows for suction fill (self-filling) from remote tank. The ability to lift material up to six foot for self loading purposes is required.

C.   INLET PLUMBING - The pump inlet plumbing will be 2" and will consist of 2" fittings and will allow unrestricted flow to the main pump (no line strainers allowed). A ball valve will be installed between the tank and pump. All necessary valves, fittings, and hose for sprayer operation, filling, and draining are included. A poly coupler with stainless steel cam levers will be installed on the pump inlet for easy pump and plumbing service. All plumbing fittings that are exposed to de-ice product will be constructed of glass-filled polypropylene or stainless steel. All valves to be glass filled polypropylene with stainless steel bolts and are to be conveniently located for operator use. Inlet valving shall allow bottom loading using main product pump or ground transfer pump.

D.   OUTLET PLUMBING - The pump outlet plumbing will consist of all necessary valves, fittings, and hose for sprayer operation, including a line-strainer and pressure gauge. A cam-lever quick coupler will be installed on the pump outlet for easy pump removal or transfer hose attachment. All plumbing fittings that are exposed to de-ice product will be constructed of glass filled polypropylene or stainless steel. All valves to be glass filled polypropylene with stainless steel bolts and to be conveniently located for operator use. Outlet valving will allow for return to agitation, 2" loading, recirculation of facility storage tanks, transferring of material to other units, and unrestricted flow to rate control components.

III.   COMPUTER RATE CONTROL SYSTEM

A.   CONSOLE - The computer rate control system consists of a computer control console and a mechanical switch box. The computer console accepts inputs for calibration and operation, and displays the flow control system information. The mechanical switchbox allows the operation of up to ten boom on/off valves. The wiring assembly attaches to the console with a single connector for quick removal.

B.   FEATURES - Control console will have five product automated rate control, 10 boom capability. A large 9" x 1-1/2" matrix LCD displays actual application rate AND data for all five products simultaneously. Audible and visual vacuum and flow alarms are integrated into the console. The control console will have download capability for direct connection to a portable computer (no data link required). Calibrations and totals must be stored in a non-volatile memory. The five-product control feature must render the console capable of controlling four injection systems and perform carrier control to utilize the unit for roadside spraying at a later date. Each of the five products on the control console can be user programmed to perform independently, for multiple width applications, (residual spraying and broadleaf control applied at the same time on different boom sections). For hand gun and invert emulsion systems, the system can be programmed to control the chemical concentration as a percentage to carrier total flow.

Under normal operation, the flow rate must be controllable either automatically or manually. When in the automatic mode, the control console will adjust the flow output to maintain programmed application rate when speed or boom width is changed. When in the manual mode, the console must adjust the flow output when the increase/decrease switch is operated. Data menu feature must give the operator the capability to pre-program a determined amount that can be increased or decreased when the unit is operational. US. acres (or lane miles), metric, or 1000 SqFt units are the available units of measure. Data readouts include boom width in inches, (includes, speed calibration, meter calibration, valve calibration and rate calibration factors), distance, speed, total and field areas, total and field volume applied, and volume remaining for each of the five products.

IV.   DE-ICE FLOW CONTROL SYSTEM

A.   FLOW METER - The de-ice system flow meter to be a turbine style, and constructed of polypropylene material. Flow meter to have a maximum flow rate of 200 GPM, (example rate applied directly to road surface: 70 gallons per lane mile at 45 MPH 3 lanes wide equals 157.50 GPM. Example of minimum flow rate applied directly to road surface: 30 gallons per lane mile at 20 MPH 1 lane wide equal 10 GPM). Flow meter to have a 3" female NPT inlet and outlet. The flow meter to be factory calibrated with the calibration number visible on the flow meter and no re-calibration required for different product weight/gallon.

B.   CONTROL VALVE - The de-ice system control valve shall be 12-volt DC electrically operated. Butterfly valve, constructed of stainless steel, with a 2" NPT female inlet and outlet coupled to a heavy duty gear reduction motor with environmentally sealed enclosure.

C.   SHUTOFF VALVES - To include a heavy-duty gear reduction motor in an environmentally sealed enclosure, coupled to a 1" full port poly ball valve. The valve operates in 3/4 seconds. Valves to also have stainless steel ball and be 12-volt DC operated. Three required.

D.   DE-ICE 3-SECTION BOOM - The de-ice boom will consist of a rear mounted spray bar for center lane swath, and manifold assemblies on each end for left and right lane swaths. The nozzle assemblies will have 6" spacing on the main center spray bar and quick-change capability on each of the three sections, with stainless steel barbs for stream jet de-icing application. Stream jet nozzles are used to reduce plugging from mag-chloride de-icing tubing with an auto enamel finish. Boom hardware is removable receiving into de-ice skid and adjustable height. Hoses feeding the 3 sections is cam-lever coupled to boom shut-off valves. System must allow for maximum (without a pressure drop) applications of 70 gallons per lane mile (three lanes simultaneously) at 45 miles per hour and a minimum application of 30 gallons per lane mile (single lane) without changing the nozzles. Stainless steel orifices shall be available for higher and lower rates if desired.

E.   RADAR SPEED SENSOR - Radar sensor is dual beam, horizontally mounted in a vibration dampening enclosure. Radar gun to be capable of speeds up to 65 MPH. 30 MOH gun is unacceptable. Includes all cables required for operation.

V.   DEMONSTRATION OF CAPABILITIES

A.   Prior to a purchase order being awarded the successful bidder may be required to provide a demonstration of the capabilities of the unit bid. The demonstration shall be required within 7 days after notification by purchaser. Location to be determined at time of notification.

VI.   SERVICE, WARRANTY, AND INSTALLATION

A.   Lifetime toll-free telephone customer support.

B.   One year warranty on all components.

C.   On-site installation and training for basic operation and maintenance (Optional).

APPENDIX C-4
Bid Specifications for the Addition of Liquid Deicer Pre-Wet Application Equipment (Provided by WSDOT).

This retrofit will be to an existing sander unit. Plans for modification of the unit to suit the liquid deicer application specification are to be submitted for approval two weeks prior to installation work.

The intent of this specification is to describe a sprayer assembly that is mounted on a sander truck. The system will pre-wet sand or perform road surface anti-ice liquid application. The sprayer will have an automated sprayer electronic control system that will maintain a desired rate per lane mile when ground speed is changed. The control console will have radar speed sensor for monitoring ground speed. The sprayer will be fitted with components that are compatible with corrosive liquids. All components to be new, current standard production models and will be prepared and serviced for customer use.

I.   TANK AND MOUNTING ASSEMBLY

A.   TANK - Two 100 gallon poly tanks for storage of de-ice material. Tanks will be designed to be mounted on the sides of existing hopper sander unit. Dimensions to be 72" long, 25" high, 18 1/2" wide on bottom and 7 1/2" wide at the tip, with two sealed access holes on each end of top surface.

B.   TANK FITTING - Two 2" poly siphon bulkhead fittings will be installed on each end of tank. One end of the tank to have level hoses with an isolator valve installed for self-leveling of the tanks. Three 1" poly bulkhead fittings, two installed on each end of tank for return sparge jet agitation, and one installed on top of tank for vent.

C.   TANK PLUMBING - All bulkhead fittings will have poly couplings with stainless steel cam-levers. A 2" hose will be supplied for both ends of tanks, to allow equalization of tank levels. A hose will be supplied to vent both tanks into sander hopper.

D.   TANK AGITATION - Agitation covers the length of tank and includes a minimum of 6 outlet sparge venturi jet agitators. Agitation flow will be supplied main bypass pump return. Agitation will not allow product to settle into any recesses of the tank. Venturi agitators are made of chemical resistant polypropylene material.

E.   MOUNTING ASSEMBLY (OPTIONAL) - The assembly will be constructed of steel, with automotive enamel finish. All necessary brackets and plates for mounting the pumping and flow control system will be included.

II.   PUMPING SYSTEM

A.   PUMP - The main pump will be a hydraulic driven centrifugal poly pump (Hypro 9303PHM* or equal) capable of 86 GPM (gallons per minute) flow rate and 80 PSI maximum. Inlet size will be 1 1/2" NPT; outlet size, 1 1/4" NPT. Hydraulic motor capacity will be matched to existing hydraulic system.

B.   PRIMING PUMP - The main pump face plate will be fitted with a positive displacement 12 VDC pump to insure positive priming of main pump when control console is powered. This feature evacuates air from pump supply lines, protecting main pump seal, and allows for suction fill (self-filling) from remote tank.

C.   INLET PLUMBING - The pump inlet plumbing will be 2" and will allow for unrestricted flow to main pump (no line strainers allowed). Poly ball valves installed between the tank and pump, will be located for convenient operation. All necessary valves, fittings, and hose for sprayer operation, self-loading, bottom loading and draining are included. Poly couplings with stainless cam-levers will be installed on the pump inlet and all hose connections for easy pump and plumbing service.

D.   OUTLET PLUMBING - The pump outlet plumbing will consist of all necessary valves, fittings and hose for sprayer operation including a line strainer and pressure gauge. Poly couplings with stainless cam-lever will be installed on the pump outlet for easy pump removal or transfer hose attachment. Unit to be capable of transferring product to another unit.

III.   CONTROL CONSOLE

A.   FEATURES - Flow rate to read out in gallons per lane mile and can be controlled automatically or manually. When in automatic, the console will adjust flow output to maintain pre-programmed rates when speed is changed. Rate one to be a pre-set, pre-wet rate, rate two to be a pre-set, anti-ice rate per lane mile. When in manual, the console will adjust flow output when the increase/decrease switch is operated. Includes boom on/off switches and a master on/off switch. Data readouts include boom width in inches, speed cal, meter cal, valve cal, rate cals., distance, speed, total and field area, total and field volume applied, and volume remaining in tank. Rate per lane control consoles will allow direct connections to portable computer (no data link interface required). All control consoles are upwardly compatible, so new features can be added at a later date. All control consoles can be directly interfaced with SCE-PARK system.

IV.   **ANTI-ICE FLOW CONTROL SYSTEM**

    A. FLOW METER - The anti-ice system flow meter will be constructed of polypropylene material, have a maximum flow rate of 55 GPM (example rate applied directly to road surface: 65 gallons per lane mile at 45 MPH = 49 GPM, example rate applied to sand: 3 gallons per lane mile at 20 MPH = 1 GPM). Flow meter to have 1 1/4" hose inlet and outlet. The flow meter will be factory calibrated with the calibration number visible on the flow meter and no re-calibration required for different product weights.

    B. CONTROL VALVE - The anti-ice system control valve will be an electrically operated butterfly valve, constructed of polypropylene, and have a 1 1/2" NPT female inlet and outlet. Valve to be installed in closed loop bypass position. This allows for fastest response time when switching between road and sand application.

    C. SHUT-OFF VALVES - The shut-off valves will be 1" full port poly electric ball valves. The valves to have a cycle time of 3/4 of a second. Valves also to have a stainless steel ball.

    D. ANTI-ICE SINGLE LANE BOOM - The anti-ice boom will consist of a mounted spray bars for center lane application utilizing stainless straight stream orifices fitted in quickjet poly manifold assemblies. Includes hose and fittings to be attached to shut-off valves.

    E. SANDER PRE-WET APPLICATOR NOZZLE ASSEMBLY - Spraying Systems Turbo Floodjet nozzle mounted to apply de-ice material directly on sand before application to roadway, with diaphragm check for non-drip application. Includes hose and fittings to be attached to shut-off valves.

    F. RADAR SPEED SENSOR - Radar sensor is dual beam, horizontally mounted in a vibration dampening enclosure. Radar gun to be capable of speeds up to 65 MPH. 30 MPH gun in unacceptable. Includes all cables required for operation.

V.   DEMONSTRATION OF CAPABILITIES

    A. Prior to a purchase order being awarded the successful bidder may be required to provide a demonstration of the capabilities of the unit bid. The demonstration shall be required within 7 days after notification by WSDOT. Location to be determined at time of notification.

VI.   SERVICE, WARRANTY, AND INSTALLATION

    A. SERVICE - Lifetime toll-free telephone customer support.

    B. WARRANTY - One year warranty on all components.

    C. INSTALLATION - On-site installation and training for basic operation and maintenance (Optional).